MARE INDICVM

TERRY DEARY'S

TRUE STORIES

MONSTER • HORROR GHOST

SCHOLASTIC

The facts behind these stories are true. However, they have been dramatized to make them into gripping stories, and some of the characters are fictitious.

Scholastic Children's Books,
Commonwealth House, 1-19 New Oxford Street,
London WC1A 1NU, UK

A division of Scholastic Ltd
London ~ New York ~ Toronto ~ Sydney ~ Auckland
Mexico City ~ New Delhi ~ Hong Kong

Published in this edition by Scholastic Ltd, 1998

True Monster Stories
First published in the UK by Scholastic Ltd, 1992

True Horror Stories
First published in the UK by Scholastic Ltd, 1993

True Ghost Stories
First published in the UK by Scholastic Ltd, 1995

ISBN 0 590 19986 2

Printed by WSOY, Finland

Contents

True Monster Stories

True Horror Stories

True Ghost Stories

TRUE MONSTER STORIES

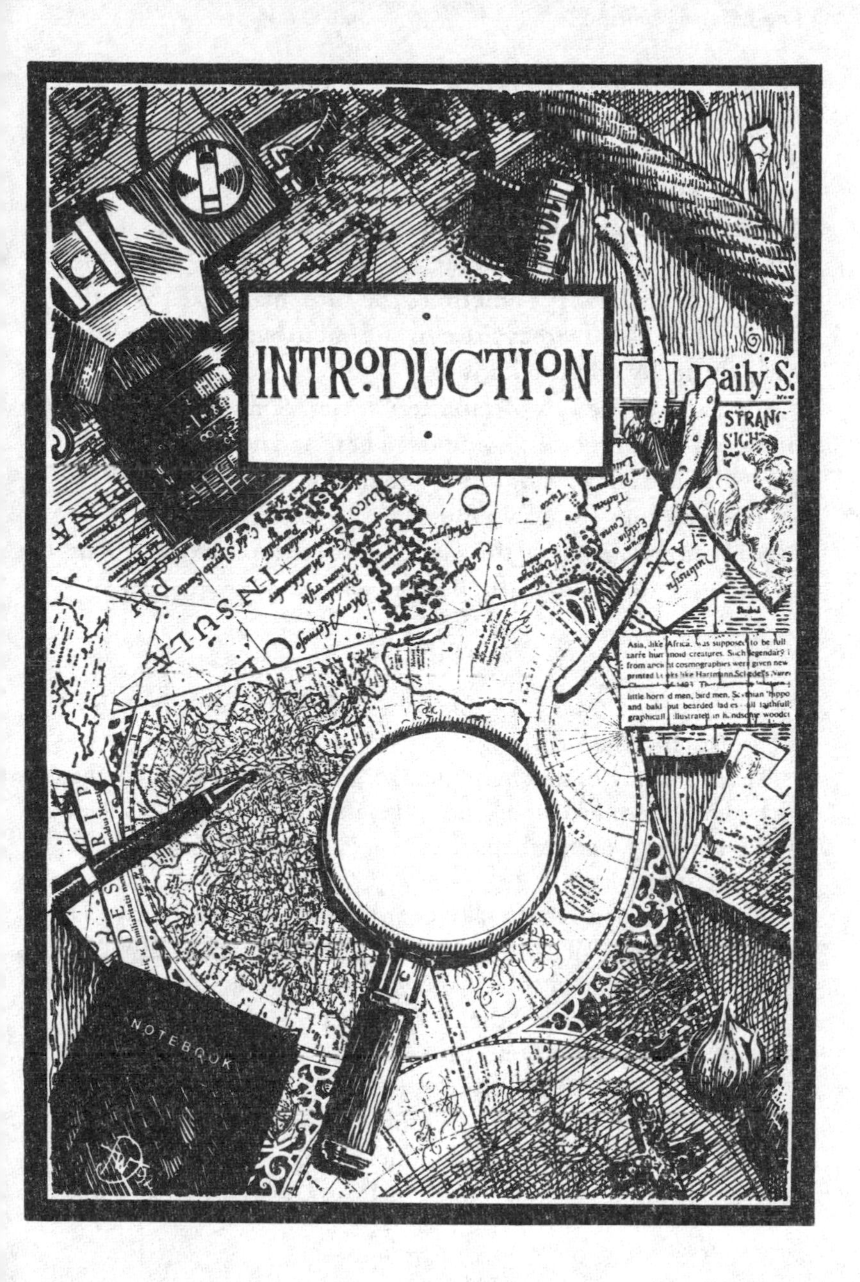
INTRODUCTION
NOTEBOOK

Monsters! Monsters! Monsters!

People have been telling stories about monsters ever since they could tell stories. They're the things that we meet in nightmares. They scare the life out of us. We love them!

What is a 'monster'? A dictionary will tell you it's a misshapen animal. Sometimes monsters are huge, like the creature in Loch Ness. Sometimes they are small, like the little vampire bat. Usually they are evil and out to harm humans. But what we really want to know is, "Are they real?"

Here is a collection of monster stories. Some from distant times and distant places. Some from here and now. Somebody, somewhere, at some time swore that each one was true. You have to make up your own mind.

All I can do is give you this clue. There are three explanations for monster stories: fibs, foolishness and facts.

Fibs

People tell lies. Many people have told monster fibs about monsters; amazing stories.

There are stories that help them explain something – like the girl who let her herd of yak die and claimed they were attacked by a giant ape man. Perhaps they were . . . but why did the ape man not attack her?

There are stories that make people sit up and take notice of you – like the man who read about the monster Bigfoot in America and decided to tell the world about the time he was kidnapped by a family of them. Perhaps he was . . . but why did he wait thirty years to tell his sensational tale?

There are stories that make you money – "Roll up, roll up! For just one dollar see the fearsome Hodag, with huge claws, bulging eyes, large horns and a line of spikes down its back!" But the Hodag was a stuffed fake of 1890s United States. So was the Fur-Bearing Trout, the Jackalope (a rabbit with antlers), the Jenny Haniver (a stuffed ray-fish moulded into a dragon shape) and many more. The great American showman, P. T. Barnum, once said of people who believe anything, "There's one born every minute." And there were thousands of what he called "suckers" ready to pay good money to see a dead, shrivelled fish. Fakes! Fibs!

Foolishness

Anyone can make a mistake. Honest, clever people make mistakes. Honest, clever people make fools of themselves over monsters.

If you're in the dark and scared, then a bat becomes a vampire and a scarecrow becomes a giant.

Two hundred years ago clever people heard tales of a monster that was as tall as a tree. It was shaped like a camel and was spotted like a leopard. They hadn't seen it, but they gave it a name: the camel-leopard. It was a monster from your worst nightmares. Would you like to meet one? Actually, you probably have. Eventually one was caught and brought into a zoo. It was given a new name – giraffe!

Not a monster and not a fib, just an honest mistake. Foolishness!

Facts

Somewhere out there in the natural world there are things we don't understand. We've heard the fibs and the foolishness of them and we're not sure if we should believe them. But if we look hard enough we can sometimes see the truth behind the stories.

Travellers back from Africa said they had seen unicorns. The *fact* is there are one-horned creatures roaming the plains. The *fact* is we call them rhinoceros.

Sailors home from the sea described mermaids. The *fact* is there are creatures called manatee which look almost human with fishy tails. Is that what they had seen?

In northern Europe people told tales of the huge Kraken. Had they seen giant squid?

Even when there are no facts to explain a monster, you have to remember the earth is very large and very old. Just because we haven't found the body or bones of a Yeti doesn't mean that it doesn't exist. There must still be things out there that we can't explain as fibs or foolishness.

They are the real monsters we are searching for.

Can you sort out the fact from the fiction? Can you find the truth about monsters in these True Monster Stories?

Enjoy finding out.

MONSTER
M·E·N

Of all the monsters, the ones that look human and act inhumanly are the most fearsome. They are the stuff of legends. The Greeks had the one-eyed, flesh-eating, giant Cyclops. They had the beautiful Siren women who lured sailors to their deaths. One of the oldest poems in the English language describes an encounter between a hero, Beowulf, and a dreadful giant, Grendel:

From the stretching moors, from the misty hollows,
Grendel came creeping
To feast his fill on the flesh of men.

The demon delayed not, but quickly clutched,
Tore men to pieces, bit through the bones,
Gulped the blood and gobbled the flesh,
Greedily gorged on the lifeless corpses.

Then the fiend stepped nearer
But Beowulf grappled and gripped him hard.
Sinews snapped and bone-joints broke
And Beowulf gained the glory of battle.

Through the ages every country has had its tales of wild men. Some were fierce and some were timid but most lived alone in forests and were very strong. They needed to be for the forests were full of wolves and bears.

There were legends about wild children being brought up by wolves and growing up as wolves. That story goes back as far as Ancient Rome. The two men who founded Rome, Romulus and Remus, were said to have been raised by a wolf after their cruel uncle left them in the wilds to die. Impossible? Well, a missionary in Bengal in the early 1900s described how he came across two such girls aged about five. The villagers rescued them from a mother wolf and he took them to an orphanage. He called them Amala, who died after just a year, and Kamala who survived a further nine years and learned to act like a human.

There was also a boy found in the jungle of Sri Lanka in 1973 who had been raised by monkeys. He could run on all fours but not stand straight or speak. There are photographs of the boy to prove that story. So wild humans are *possible* . . . and if they are evil as well as wild then they become True Monsters.

Judge each story for yourself and decide whether you think it is true.

The Wild Man of Wales

Megan was a hard woman. It was a hard life on the mountain farm. You had to be tough to survive.

She stood at the door of her cottage and watched the sun slip down behind the mountains. "Rhiannon!" she called sharply. "Carys!" It was too late for her daughters to be out, especially after what she'd heard in the chapel yesterday.

The two girls tumbled, breathless, round the farmyard wall, eyes shining and excited.

"Oh, Ma!" Rhiannon, the elder one, gasped. "You should hear what Tegwyn's been saying down in the village."

"So that's where you've been. Gossiping, is it?" their mother said harshly.

"Sorry, Ma," Carys said. "Were you worried about us?"

"Worried?" the woman snorted. "Why would I be worried?"

"In case the wild man got us," Rhiannon said breathlessly.

Her mother pushed a bowl of soup across the table towards the child. "More scared that you would get the wild man," she said and her hard mouth turned up a little at the corners.

"It's not funny, Ma!" Carys said. "Tegwyn said there was a robbery at Penlan Farm on Saturday and Aberdyfi Farm last night. He's working his way up the valley, Ma." Her bright eyes widened and her voice dropped. "They reckon it's our turn next."

"You don't want to go listening to all that wild man nonsense. I'm ashamed that Tegwyn Morris would go filling your head with such stuff!"

"It's not nonsense," Rhiannon urged. "They set a trap for him at Aberdyfi last night. They *saw* him! He had hardly any clothes, just skins they say. And he had long red shaggy hair! They saw him in the moonlight going into the barn. Dropped a net over him!"

The girl bent her head to sip the hot soup while her sister went on with the story. "But he tore his way out of it with his bare hands, Ma. He's stronger than Dyfed Evans's bull, they reckon."

Megan's eyes narrowed. She spoke quietly. "Finish that soup. Then I want you to wash, brush your hair and say your prayers, you understand?"

"Yes, Ma," the girls murmured.

"Especially your prayers. Pray your dad gets home safe from market tomorrow eh?"

"Yes, Ma."

"And forget about wild men. If you say your prayers there's nothing bad can get you – not by day and not by night. I don't want you losing any beauty sleep over it. See?"

The girls nodded and finished their meal in silence, kissed their mother and said goodnight.

Megan sat in the flickering shadows of the oil-lamp till the only sound from the girls' room was their soft snoring. She stood up and began to move briskly. First she bolted the door carefully and checked that every window was shuttered. She blew out the lamp and moved into the kitchen.

Carefully she opened the window shutter, letting the ice-bright moonlight flow over the stone-flagged floor. Something glinted in the log basket. She picked it up and returned to the window where she sat on a stool like a cat at a mouse-hole.

The moon rose higher and brighter. The only sounds were the owls in the valley and a late curlew that stirred from its sleep. The woman nodded in her chair as the hours slid past.

Then came a sound, soft as a cat's footstep.

Megan stiffened and strained her eyes. Something in the shadows of the barn was moving. A gentle rattle at the barn door . . . but that was firmly shut. Nothing there. Her hand clutched the thing from the log basket. The other hand reached out and touched the big black Bible on the table.

"Behold, I come as a thief," she murmured, remembering the chapel lessons from her childhood.

One shadow, edged with silver, moved away from the barn and into the moonlight shining on the cobbled yard. A man. A huge and almost shapeless bundle of rags. He was drawn to the open shutter like a moth to a candle flame. Megan froze in the shadow and shrank against the wall.

She could hear his harsh breathing, smell the stench from his animal clothes and finally, see the filthy clawed hand reaching through the open window. Megan's mouth was dry. But her hand was wet with sweat where it was wrapped around the axe from the log basket. She swept the axe down as expertly as she did when she was splitting logs. There was a wail like a wounded dog as the stranger tumbled back out of the window . . . and the hand jumped onto the kitchen floor.

Megan breathed out for the first time in minutes. She watched the sobbing creature stagger across the yard and into the valley. With a shaking hand she lit the lamp and turned the Bible to her favourite chapter. "Resist the devil and he will flee from you," she said.

She stayed awake all that night, reading. As the first light turned the sky slate grey she took the severed hand in a cloth and wrapped herself in a shawl. She knew her children would be safe now.

Megan hurried down to the village and found tired men gathering at the market cross. "Sorry, Megan, no sign of the wild man," Tegwyn Evans said.

But Megan opened the cloth and showed the men. "I think if you follow the trail of blood from my house you will find him."

As the sun rose they found the trail and followed it to a cave hidden behind a waterfall. But the wild man was gone. He never returned to Nanhrynan. Yet, still today, that place is called the Cave of Owen Langoch – the Cave of the Red-haired man.

But that wild man was no match for a caring mother.

Monster Men – FACT FILE

1. The wild man legend almost killed the king of France. In 1392 Charles VI went to a carnival with friends. They dressed as the legendary wild men with masks of tar and paper. Someone took a torch to peer more closely at the dancers and the costumes burst into flames. Charles's mother saved him by smothering him with a cloak. His four friends died.

2. A Scottish mountain has its own giant. This mountain, Ben MacDhui in the Cairngorms, has the Big Grey Man. Many very experienced climbers claim to have seen him. The huge, grey figure has feet like a bird of prey and pointed ears. It must be difficult to see them though – they are about 6 metres off the ground!

3. Not all wild men were reported to be hairy. Some were covered with leaves or moss. They were, naturally enough, known as Green Men. Groups of actors, called Mummers, still dress up as Green Men to perform in country festivals.

4. In the Alps there is a legend of a wild woman. She can charm men in spite of her ugliness. She has tremendous strength and has a taste for eating children! Could this be the source of the witch in the Hansel and Gretel story?

5. The tallest recorded man was Robert Pershing Wadlow who was born in the United States in 1918. He was 2.72 metres tall, but soon outgrew his strength and died at the age of 22.

6. In the Bible there is a description of King Nebuchadnezzar, who "was driven from men and did eat grass like an ox. His body was wet with the dew of heaven till his hair grew like eagles' feathers and his nails like birds' claws."

7. If Goliath was really 6 cubits tall, as the Bible story says, then he would measure 2.9 metres. The earliest Greek version of the Bible says he was 4 Greek cubits – 2.08 metres – which is much more likely.

8. Wild men are said to have appeared as wolves (usually called werewolves), as leopards (in Africa in the 1930s) and even as owls. At the time of the sighting of the sea monster Morgawr in Cornwall, a sixteen-year-old girl swore she saw "a monster like a devil flying up through the trees near old Mawnan church." The girl and her friend admitted that they thought it was someone dressed up in an owl costume for a joke. But when the man took off and flew into a tree they were pretty surprised.

9. In England in the 1200s a wild man was caught by fishermen in the North Sea. A monk at that time wrote that the man was very strong and lived on raw fish.

Apart from being unusually hairy he was like a human in every way – he wasn't a merman. After a few months his captors tired of him and he escaped, never to be seen again.

10. Just as Yeti, Yowie and Bigfoot are believed to be descendants of the ancient Gigantopithecus ape, so some people believe that wild men are remnants of the prehistoric Neanderthal man.

Some monster men are fakes, not true monsters or unknown creatures at all but men with a cruelly twisted sense of humour. Perhaps one such man roamed the streets of Victorian London, terrorising women fifty years before the famous Jack the Ripper appeared on the scene.

Perhaps it was all a wicked joke. At the time there was no mystery about the monster. It seemed that everyone knew who he was. But he was never caught in the act and he was too well known and important a person to be arrested just on rumours.

Yet this mystery remains. If he was a normal human with a nasty sense of humour, where did he get the power to escape capture by leaping over walls and fences where no policeman could ever follow? For that was how he got his name . . .

Spring-Heeled Jack

18 February 1838

Green Dragon Alley was cold and Green Dragon Alley was dark. But on that night Green Dragon Alley was the lair of something more fearful than a dragon.

The stinking streets of London were no place for two young ladies that night. Anyone with any sense was at home sitting in front of a blazing coal fire. The smoke from the fires thickened the dark city air. But Lucy and Margaret Scales were out in the dank and deserted streets. They lifted their skirts to step through the mixture of mud and rubbish. They shivered in their shawls, put their heads down and hurried home.

"We shouldn't have left it so late!" Margaret moaned.

"Don't be silly," Lucy sighed. "We'll be safe if we stay together." But Lucy didn't sound too sure of that.

Margaret clung to the sleeve of her sister's dress and groaned again. "I think my feet are going to drop off with tiredness."

"No they are not!" her sister said firmly. "Just stand here a while and rest," she ordered and leaned against a street lamp.

"Read the newspaper to me again," Margaret whispered.

Lucy pulled out the torn page from her purse. She held it up to catch the flickering orange light. "It says, '*Peckham Prowler Puzzles Police*' . . ."

"Go on," Margaret urged.

Her sister read on. " 'Last night the Lord Mayor of London, Sir John Cowan, made a sensational statement to the gentlemen of the press at Mansion House. Sir John claimed that he had received a letter signed *A Peckham Resident*. The letter claimed that a person of high rank had made a bet that he would disguise himself and scare thirty people to death . . .' "

"Ohh!" Margaret whimpered. "Just the thought of it is scaring me to death."

Lucy went on, " 'He has already succeeded in frightening seven ladies out of their senses. Two of the ladies are not likely to recover. The writer asked, what were the police going to do about the man? The mayor announced that the police would be putting every effort into catching this deranged man. They were puzzled because he has appeared in so many disguises. He has appeared as a white bull, as a bear, and as a baboon. He has been seen wearing shining armour and in Hackney as a lamplighter who walked on his hands and carried his ladders between his feet. Sir John said that extra police will patrol the area until this evil man is caught.' "

Margaret gave a small cry. "He could be anywhere."

"Well, he's not here," Lucy snapped. "Come on, Margaret. We're almost at Green Dragon Alley then we're home. Do you feel well enough?"

"No–o. I wish we hadn't gone to see George tonight."

"We always go to see George on Wednesday evenings – and no mad man is going to stop me," said Lucy. "Anyway, since the mayor made that speech no one has seen this Peckham

Prowler . . . and that's five or six weeks ago now. Take my word for it, Margaret, we're safe."

"Just read that last piece," her sister said.

Lucy peered at the paper and said, " 'Police claim their attempts to catch the man have only failed because the man has such power to leap to great heights. It is believed that he must have springs in his boots. The terrified people of London have already given this monster a name – they call him Spring-Heeled Jack!' "

"Spring-Heeled Jack!" Margaret breathed. "I think I'll stay here till a policeman comes."

"Don't be so stupid. You'll freeze to death."

"I don't care!"

"Once we're past Green Dragon Alley we're safe!"

"I'm not moving till I see a policeman."

"Then you can stay here until Spring-Heeled Jack comes and gets you!" her sister said and walked off into the mist.

"Don't leave me!" Margaret squeaked and hurried after Lucy who had already reached the corner of Green Dragon Alley. But Margaret slithered on the slimy cobbles and stumbled onto her knees.

Margaret was never able to remember very clearly what happened next. It was too quick . . . and too incredible.

Lucy had stopped on the corner of Green Dragon Alley to wait for Margaret. Suddenly a dark shadow leapt out from the alley and stood behind Lucy. Margaret tried to scream but no sound came from her frightened throat. Lucy turned slowly and came face to face with the monstrous man.

As Margaret watched, the man leaned forward and breathed a gust of fire into his victim's face.

The fog swallowed the sound as Lucy fell in a dead faint. It swallowed too the dark, leaping figure with the bulging eyes.

Spring-Heeled Jack had left the poor people of Peckham in

peace for five weeks. But now he was back with a new and nasty trick. For, when Margaret reached her sister, Lucy's pale face was scorched and her hair singed.

From far away, through the fog, there came a cackle of evil laughter.

20 February 1838

Jane Alsop ran to the front door of her parents' house. Someone was ringing the bell wildly.

She threw open the door and at first saw no one in the dim street. Then a man called to her from the shadows of the pavement. "For God's sake, bring a light! I am a policeman. We have just caught Spring-Heeled Jack in the lane!"

The girl hurried to obey and returned to the door a few seconds later with a candle.

As she handed it to the 'policeman' he threw off his huge cloak. He appeared to be wearing a tight-fitting helmet on his head, and a shiny, white suit. His eyes bulged and sparkled in the light of a candle.

Suddenly he breathed across the candle. A ball of flame burst into Jane's face. As she staggered back, half blinded, he clutched at her with claws like a bird of prey and ripped her dress.

Jane's screams brought her sisters, Mary and Sarah, running. Sarah tore Jane from the monster's grasp, pulled her back into the house and managed to slam the door.

Spring-Heeled Jack had carried out his most vicious and daring raid yet. The young women of London were not safe even in their own homes. He was the worst kind of monster.

Spring-Heeled Jack – FACT FILE

1. Spring-Heeled Jack became a legend in his own time. He became the popular hero (or villain) of short thriller stories known as 'penny dreadfuls'. The character also appeared in popular theatre shows of the time.

2. A lot of fiction was written about him. In time he turned from being a villain to being a kind of super-hero. The result was that over the years people tended to forget he really existed. Some writers have claimed that he was just a legend created by servants to explain accidents and thefts in the home.

3. Attacks by Spring-Heeled Jack were reported, on and off, for the next 66 years. By the last one in 1904 the original Jack must have been 80 or 90 years old! He was also sighted in many parts of the country. It is clear that there were many copy-cat Jacks.

4. Some people suggested that Jack was a mad circus fire-eater. Others said he was a kangaroo dressed up by a lunatic animal trainer.

5. The most believable suggestion was that Jack was in fact the young Lord Waterford who would have been about 27 or 28 at the time of the first attacks. The clues pointing to him are:

Lord Waterford was a well-known practical joker; he had bulging eyes;

Spring-Heeled Jack had the letter 'W' on the front of his white suit;
Lord Waterford was always in London at the time of Spring-Heeled Jack's activities;
Lord Waterford was a great athlete, quite capable of out-running and out-jumping police;
he was noted for his cruelty to people and animals.

6. Lord Waterford settled down to a quiet married life in 1842, by which time the attacks had stopped. When they started again they were obviously the work of someone else.

7. In 1845 a Spring-Heeled Jack caused his first death. Thirteen-year-old Maria Davis was cornered by a fire-breathing man and thrown into a muddy ditch where she slowly drowned.

8. A Spring-Heeled Jack was caught in 1845. He was leaping over hedges and walls with shrieks and groans in West London. It turned out to be a young butcher from Brentford. He was too young to have been the attacker in 1838.

9. In 1877 a Spring-Heeled Jack appeared, breathing fire, at an army barracks in Aldershot. The guard fired at him and scared him off but didn't hurt him. Jack gained the reputation for being magically shielded from bullets. In fact the guard had fired blanks.

10. In 1944 a similar character appeared in Mattoon Town, Illinois. He wore a tight-fitting suit and a gas mask. People who saw him standing outside their open bedroom window became ill the next day. They claimed the Mad Gasser of Mattoon was spraying deadly fumes into the air. Who he was, where he came from and where he went remains a mystery.

MONSTER
BIRDS

Monsters that swoop down from the skies and carry off their victims are every bit as horrifying as the ones that lurk in the woods and the caves of earth, or the dark depths of lakes and oceans. Since the days of the Pterodactyls, death has hovered in the skies. The flying dinosaurs are long dead, but some of their descendants, the birds, are still sometimes believed to be a threat to humans . . . especially children . . .

The Thunderbird

An old man looked over the parched Missouri plains. His skin was dry and wrinkled as parchment and his eyes glinted watery blue in the sunlight. Sad eyes. Eyes that had seen a monster and would never forget.

He sat in the afternoon sun, still as death, the old eyes fixed on the faded blue sky.

"Good day!" a young hiker called, uncertainly. He had thick walking boots, and a large back pack. Around his neck he carried expensive binoculars.

After a few moments the old man turned his gaze towards the hiker and nodded in greeting.

"Nice day," the young man grinned.

The old man thought about it for a moment. Then he jerked his head forward on his scrawny neck and hissed, "Not much cover out there on the plain!"

The hiker stepped back. "No-o," he agreed. "But what would you want cover for?"

The old man narrowed his eyes and murmured, "From the bird."

The young man gave a small sigh and dropped his pack on the dusty earth. He tapped his binoculars. "I'm interested in bird-watching too," he grinned. "I'm Al . . . Al Duncan." He stretched out a hand.

"Edward Colgin," the old man grunted and shook hands with a fierce grip that made the hiker's eyes water.

"You want to have a look through my binoculars?" Al offered.

"I may look old but my eyes are sharper than a timber-wolf's tooth," Edward sniffed.

"Cost fifty dollars," the young man boasted. "Made in Germany! You'll see your birds much clearer with these," he offered again.

Old Edward's face hardened. "I won't need no fancy eyeglasses for the bird I'm waiting for. It's big enough."

"Ah, you're looking for eagles, are you? I heard there were plenty round here."

Edward shook his head slowly. "Not eagles. Bigger than that."

Al scratched his head. "Won't get anything bigger than an eagle in Missouri," he shrugged.

Edward Colgin turned on him fiercely. "Oh, you know that, do you? You know that for a fact?"

"Well . . ."

"Because I happen to know that there is a bigger bird. Bigger than any bird you've ever seen."

Al laughed nervously. "What sort of bird's that, Mr Colgin?"

The old man stared hard at the sky. "The Thunderbird."

The young hiker gasped. "That's an Indian legend . . . just a story. We learned it at school."

"You did, did you?" Edward said quietly.

"Yeah! It was the Illini tribe, wasn't it? They called it 'the-bird-that-eats-humans" – the *piasa*. But that was a hundred years ago. Teacher used to tell us how Ouatogo killed it."

"He did, did he?" the old man snorted.

"Yes," Al went on eagerly. "He stood out in the open and

waited for the *piasa* to attack. But twenty of his warriors were hiding in the rocks. As the bird swooped on Ouatogo they killed it with their arrows." The hiker chuckled. "So even if you believe the legend, the creature was killed."

"Is that a fact?" Edward grunted sourly. He stared back into the glare of the autumn sky and said, "Then I'll tell you another story. But this story just happens to be true. It happened just fifty years ago – back in 1878 in Tippah County. That's Tippah County on the other side of the river, see it?"

Al sank down onto his back pack and nodded.

"The farmers had lost a lot of stock that autumn. The settlers had driven the wildlife off the plains. The birds of prey had nothing left to catch. So they turned on the farm animals. Those farmers complained about the pigs and the sheep they were losing – reckoned it was eagles. But they were wrong."

"But how do you know, Mr Colgin?" Al insisted.

The old man didn't seem to hear the question. He was looking at the blank, blue sky and seeing pictures from fifty years before. "Of course, no one believed the birds could harm people. An eagle couldn't attack a human, could it? So they got careless. It was a Thursday. Recess. The school teacher let the kids out into the field to play then went back in to have a coffee. The next thing he knew there were screams from the field. He dashed out in time to see a huge bird rising into the air . . . with an eight-year-old boy in his claws." Edward Colgin swallowed hard and his sharp eyes seemed to cloud for a few moments. "Poor little Jemmie Kenney."

The young hiker stretched out a hand and laid it on the old man's arm. "An eagle?"

The old man shook his head and sniffed. "Too big. Two or even three times the size of an eagle."

"A Thunderbird?"

"I can still hear the screams of poor little Jemmie," Edward said hoarsely. "Struggled so hard the bird had to drop him . . . dropped him practically at my feet."

"Dead?"

The old man snorted. A question too stupid to deserve an answer.

"You were there, Mr Colgin?"

"I was the teacher. I was to blame. I let the Thunderbird kill Jemmie Kenney."

"You can't say that, Mr Colgin."

"The rest of Tippah County did," the teacher said bitterly. "Lost my job. Had to turn to keeping pigs. The Thunderbird killed part of me when he killed Jemmie Kenney," he said.

Al shook his head. "You didn't ought to blame yourself, Mr Colgin. Nothing you can do about it now."

The old man's thin lips turned up in a grim smile. "Oh, no? Aren't you forgetting that story about old Ouatogo?"

"You mean that's why you're sitting out here? Bait? Waiting for the Thunderbird to attack again?" Al cried. He didn't believe it. Still he glanced nervously up into the empty sky . . . the almost empty sky. High above a small dot circled.

Al jumped to his feet and fumbled with his binoculars. His trembling hands couldn't hold them steady and they fell to the ground. But he didn't need them now. For the dot was falling towards them and growing bigger every second. Al began to back away down the dusty trail. "But Mr Colgin . . . Ouatogo had twenty warriors hiding in the rocks!"

The old man sat calm as the rocks on the hillside. The bird cast a shadow over the path. Edward Colgin slid a hand inside his shirt and gently pulled out a huge Colt pistol. "Fifty years, I've waited, Jemmie, fifty years!"

The young man screamed and the old man laughed as a huge bird began to fill the sky above his head . . .

Monster Birds – FACT FILE

1. In 1878 Jemmie Kenney was indeed snatched by a huge bird while his teacher looked on helplessly. But scientists have claimed that an eagle could lift nothing larger than a fawn or young goat. So what sort of bird took Jemmie?

2. The largest known living bird is the Wandering Albatross with a wingspan of 3.3 metres, but that was only ever seen in the southern oceans. An Arctic expedition claimed to have measured a Wandering Albatross at 4. 22 metres but this was not confirmed.

3. The largest known extinct bird is the Terahorn, which had a truly monstrous 7.5-metre wingspan. Fossils have been found in the Southern United States (where Jemmie was snatched) – but it died out at least 10 000 years ago . . . didn't it?

4. Some native American Indians claim they still see the Thunderbird today. They describe it as bigger than an aeroplane. The Illini tribe says it has horns and red eyes. The Haida tribe believes that the Thunderbird is a form of human ghost.

5. After the death of Jemmie Kenney there were regular reports of giant birds in the United States. They have also been blamed for some mysterious disappearances. Some sightings say the birds had a wingspan of over 5 metres.

6. Giant birds have been reported in Europe too. Marie Delex was taken by a large bird in 1838 in Switzerland. Her body was found a couple of months later. As a small five-year-old it's believable. But 100 years later, Svanhild Hantvigsen claimed that as a three-year-old in Norway she was taken to an eagle's nest . . . and she lived to tell the tale! That story is harder to believe.

7. In 1976 there was a series of reported attacks in Texas by a huge winged creature. The witnesses swore it was a Pteranodon. These flying reptiles are supposed to have become extinct 64 million years ago. Explanations are:

The witnesses saw rare local birds;
Pteranodons survived, unknown to humans;
there was a time warp in that place and witnesses had glimpses of prehistoric skies.

8. Reports of creatures that are half-human, half-bird are even more common than sightings of prehistoric creatures. In Point Pleasant, West Virginia in 1966 a bat-winged man making a squeaking noise like a large mouse chased a car which was doing 100 miles per hour (160 kph). The creature became known as Mothman. Several sightings that year established that he was 1.5 to 2 metres tall, grey-brown in colour and headless. He had a pair of glowing, red eyes where his shoulders should be and a wingspan of about 3 metres.

9. Not many known birds of prey measure up to the descriptions of monster birds. The Andean Condor of South America can weigh 11.3 kg and a Californian Condor is claimed to have reached 14.1 kg. Could such a bird carry a human child weighing more than itself? In October 1991 in Cairns, Australia, a six-year-old girl was lifted 30 metres into the air . . . on the end of a kite! She fell from about 15 metres and luckily survived.

10. The biggest bird of legend was the Roc which featured in the story of Sinbad. It fed elephants to its young. When Sinbad annoyed it the Roc picked up a boulder, dropped it on one of Sinbad's ships and sank it. Impossible? Yes, but the Arabian sailors probably did come across the real live Elephant Bird when they sailed to Madagascar. It looked like an ostrich but laid eggs six times the size of ostrich's eggs – that's about 148 times the size of a chicken's egg. Sadly it became extinct about 500 years ago.

T·H·E
LOCHNESS
MONSTER

The Loch Ness Monster is probably the most famous monster in the world today. Thousands of people have reported it – no one has yet proved it exists. Look at these two stories and some of the facts, then make up your own mind . . .

The Legend

The day was hot and getting hotter. The monks trudged onwards, tired and thirsty, their rough wool robes growing warm and itchy. One young monk looked up towards the purple Scottish mountain shimmering in the heat. Still five weary miles to go. Then he looked towards the cool, deep water of the lake the locals called Loch Ness.

The monk licked his dry lips and hurried forward to where the leader strode along the shoreline. "Father Columba! Father Columba!" he panted.

The old monk turned and frowned. "Yes, my son?"

"Could we . . . could I stop for a swim?" he asked nervously.

Father Columba looked at him for a long while, then his stern face softened. "Of course, Edwin. It will do us all good to rest."

Edwin put down his bundle, pulled the rope from his waist and tugged the heavy habit over his head. Even in this heat the wind off the loch was cool and made him shudder. The water was dark brown with the peat washed down by the mountain stream. Suddenly it looked unfriendly.

But the other monks were sitting by the edge of the water soaking their dusty feet and urging Edwin on.

"What's the matter?" one called. "Scared the Kelpie's going to get you?"

"The what?" Edwin asked nervously.

"The Kelpie," Father Columba nodded. "They say the natives worship a water spirit called a Kelpie. One lives in every lake in this land."

"We Christians don't believe such things!" the young monk laughed, uncertain. Then he asked, "What sort of water spirit?"

"A monster," one monk teased. "A huge and hungry monster. He'd swallow you in one bite then spit out the bones."

"There's no such thing," Edwin said.

The other monk shrugged and asked, "Then why not dive in?"

So, to save his pride, young Edwin had to walk forward into the dark water. It was freezing, so cold it numbed his skin first

then made it tingle. His teeth chattered. The water came up to his waist. He dipped till his shoulders went under the water. He gasped with the shock, then pushed forward into a slow swimming stroke. The monks on the pebbled beach gave an encouraging cheer. He rolled onto his back to wave at them.

Suddenly the cheers turned to cries of horror. Edwin saw them stare in wonder at some point high above his head. He turned and saw it.

The monster towered out of the water twice as high as a man. It had a head like a snake and a gaping mouth. The skin was dark as wet leather. But worst were the eyes: small and evil and looking straight at him.

Edwin struggled to turn but the weed seemed to catch at his feet and drag him back. The monster slid silently forward and opened its lipless mouth further. The young monk flapped at the water like a wounded duck. The other monks had backed away from the water's edge and some fell on their knees to pray.

But Father Columba stepped forward and clutched the wooden cross he wore around his neck. Raising the wooden cross towards the creature he ordered it back to its home in hell where it belonged.

Edwin heard the water bubble and gurgle like a boiling pot as the monster sank. The fear made him faint and the water sucked at him. His limp body slipped below the water. By the time the frightened monks had dragged his body from the freezing water it was too late.

"Dead," an old monk muttered.

On the slopes above Loch Ness some local people gathered. They'd seen Father Columba drive the monster off. Still, the creature's power was great enough to kill this Christian newcomer. Columba knew he had to act or all the monks' good work would be of no use.

He knelt down and laid a hand upon young Edwin's body as he said an urgent prayer. The natives shook their heads in wonder. Edwin coughed, he groaned, he sat up and clung to old Columba.

The story of the miracle was written down a hundred long years later. It is the first report in writing that we have about a creature in the loch. Columba found his place in history and became a saint.

Yet it is the monster that is better remembered. Known and wondered at all around the world. Known today by everyone as the famous Loch Ness Monster.

The Loch Ness Monster was forgotten for hundreds of years. Then in 1933, a new road was built around the loch. New views of it had been opened up to many more people. If the monster was in the habit of popping up for a look at the world then it was just a matter of time before it would be seen, and photographed . . . by someone. That first someone was Mr Hugh Gray. On his way home from church on 13 November 1933 he saw a disturbance in the loch and took five photographs. They weren't clear photographs. They didn't prove a thing. But they started off the monster hunt that's been going on ever since.

People began to 'remember' seeing a monster thirty or fifty years before. They said they hadn't reported it at the time for fear of being laughed at. Others retold stories of 'sightings' over the centuries right back to Saint Columba's adventure.

That was when the monster hunters came to Loch Ness. Some of the hunters may have been out for a bit of fun. But others took the monster – and their hunting skills – very seriously.

Who in the world was the best person to seek and capture a huge, wild creature? A big game hunter, of course. Someone skilled in tracking and snaring wildlife in Africa. If he could capture rhinos and elephants in Africa then surely he could capture this thing in a Scottish loch, couldn't he?

The great day arrived when the Big Game Hunter moved into the lakeside hotel. He was met by reporters after a good story. He was keenly watched by locals who were interested in seeing the great man . . . and by someone who was interested in a little mischievous fun . . .

The Monster Hunter

"Mr Wetherall! Mr Wetherall!" a girl cried. "I'm from the *Daily Mail*. I'm Sally Jarvis. Can we talk about your expedition?"

Mr Wetherall looked down his fine nose at the eager girl. "I don't like interviews," he said coldly.

Sally blinked. "But, Mr Wetherall, my newspaper is paying all your expenses to come here. Surely part of the deal is that you let us know what's happening?"

The explorer sighed, settled on a stool at the hotel bar and sniffed, "Oh, very well. Just this once."

Sally was upset to discover that reporters from the other newspapers had their notepads at the ready. Ready to snap up her story. She didn't notice the two locals who sat at the end of the bar, listening with quiet smiles on their faces.

"Could you tell me a little about your plans?" Sally asked.

"I plan to track down the Loch Ness Monster and probably capture it," the great man said.

Sally seemed doubtful. "But in the past year hundreds of people have tried to do that. Why are you so sure that you will succeed where they failed?"

The explorer raised his eyebrows. "They were amateurs. I am an expert. I am a member of the Royal Geographical Society. You don't become a member of the Royal Geographical Society unless you are a skilled and experienced scientist."

"How do you plan to find Nessie?" a man called out, to Sally's annoyance. This was *her* interview.

Wetherall smiled. "By using science. This creature has been seen on land. There are reports of it crossing the road and diving back into the water. There are too many trees and cliffs for the creature to do this in many places. There are only a certain number of places where the creature can enter and leave the loch. I shall look there. That is the scientific way to do it."

"But how will you find traces where no one else has?" Sally asked quickly.

The great man stroked his fine moustache calmly. "Because, young lady, I *know* what I'm looking for."

At the corner of the bar one local turned to the other. "And when you know what you want to find you very often find it."

They left the hotel and laughed all the way back to their boarding house. As they stepped through the front door they paused. In the hallway was a stand to hold umbrellas. It was made from the foot of a hippopotamus. Carefully the two men began to take out the umbrellas and place them on the floor . . .

The report in the *Daily Mail* caused a sensation all over the world. Within a week the great explorer had found footprints of the monster, just as he'd said he would.

"... It is a four-fingered beast and it has feet or pads about 20cm across ... I am convinced it can breathe like a hippopotamus or a crocodile. The tracks I found were only a few hours old, clearly demonstrating that the animal is in the neighbourhood where I expected to find it."

Everyone at the *Daily Mail* was delighted with Wetherall's story. Everyone, that is, except their reporter at Loch Ness. As the great explorer sat in the bar he was surrounded by admirers who wanted to hear his story. Everyone was buying him drinks. Everyone except the two locals who smiled quietly at the corner of the bar.

Sally pushed through to the great man. "Ah, my girl!" he called. "Happy with your story?"

She shook her head slowly. The crowd in the bar grew quiet as the reporter said softly, "There's been a report from some experts on the copies that you made of the footprints."

Wetherall looked at her sharply. "Confirming my theory," he said confidently.

"Er . . . no."

The bar was as silent as the bottom of Loch Ness.

"The report says that all the footprints are the same," Sally said carefully.

"Of course they're the same!" Wetherall exploded. "They're from the same creature, you stupid girl."

She shook her head. "No. I mean exactly the same. It's the same footprint over and over again."

For a while the crowd around him was silent. Suddenly someone called out, "So the Loch Ness Monster has only one leg!"

A roar of laughter broke out as Wetherall turned scarlet. "There must be some mistake!"

"Have to call it the *hop* Ness Monster! Can you imagine a twenty-ton tennis ball? Boing! Boing! Boing!" another man cried.

Wetherall fled. In fact he resigned from the Royal Geographical Society not long after and went all the way back to Africa.

And in the bar room of the lakeside hotel two locals took out a parcel and unwrapped it on the bar. The hippopotamus foot stood there while the bar room crowd jeered, "Boing! Boing! Boing!"

It was the first of many such tricks played with the legend of the Loch Ness Monster.

After all, if you know what you want to find you very often find it . . .

Loch Ness Monster – FACT FILE

1. If the creature in the loch is indeed a survivor from prehistoric times then there can be no Loch Ness *Monster*. If there *is* anything then there must be a family of Loch Ness *Monsters* for them to have bred and survived.

2. There have been 10 000 *reported* sightings but only about 3 000 of these have been *recorded*. There are about 20 photographs of 'things' in Loch Ness and 25 films or videos. There seems to be a curse on attempts to photograph the monster. Many sightings have been disbelieved because cameras jammed at a vital moment or the film turned out mysteriously blank. Underwater radar explorations (sonar) have come up with some fakes, some mistakes (shoals of fish) and some blank results. Underwater photographs taken in 1975 have produced pictures that could be the flipper of a type of water dinosaur called a Plesiosaur. Plesiosaurs are thought to have become extinct millions of years ago.

3. Loch Ness is the largest body of fresh water in the British Isles. It is over 300 metres deep in places and 22 miles (35 km) long. Its size makes it hard to explore and the colour of the water adds to the problems. Peat is washed down from the mountains around and makes the water dark brown. On the other hand Loch Ness would be a good place for a monster to live because it is full of fish: salmon, trout and eels. Some people believe

that the monsters escape underwater detection by hiding in deep caves. But there are no underwater caves in Loch Ness. This has been proved by underwater radar scans. There are, however, underwater currents which cause 'standing waves' to appear even on the calmest of days. These often have been mistaken for monstrous 'humps'.

4. A clear and 'razor sharp' film of the creature was apparently taken in the 1930s by a banker called Currie. But he refused to show the film until "the public takes such matters seriously." It was never shown, and since his death it has not been found.

5. A whisky company offered a reward of a million pounds to anyone who could capture the Loch Ness Monster. Their money is safe. For, if someone did present them with a real monster, it would be worth many, many millions of pounds in television, newspaper, film and book rights.

6. Many of the witness reports are alike – and that suggests they have really seen something. They agree that the monster is 8 to 12 metres in length, with dark, thick skin and a small head on the end of a long neck. But not all witnesses are *reliable*. Mr and Mrs Spicer provided a sensational witness report of the monster crossing the road in front of their car on 22 July 1933. At first Mr Spicer said it was 2 metres long . . . but three years later he was saying it could have been 9 metres long.

7. Some people don't believe Nessie is a creature at all, but a spaceship from Venus. Others are convinced it is the ghost of an ancient creature that haunts the loch. In 1973 The Reverend D. Omand tried to 'exorcise' the ghost with prayers.

8. Scientists have tried to explain the monster in many ways. They say witnesses saw large otters, giant eels, seals, swimming deer, diving birds, rotting tree-trunks, shoals of fish and even whales.

9. Old stories tell of an island in the loch which was swallowed up one night, and of a lazy monk from St Cummein. He refused to plough the land beside the church; a monstrous water-horse from the loch ploughed it for him, then vanished . . . taking the lazy monk with it! Ireland has many *loughs* (their name for lochs) and several tales of Saints defeating *lough piasts* (lake monsters): Saint Mochua of Balla thwarted a monster in a Connaught lough while Saint Patrick tricked a monster into imprisoning itself in a large barrel.

10. A film company went to Loch Ness in 1969 to make a film in which Nessie had to appear. They hired a submarine to tow a model Nessie for the film. As the submarine explored the loch its sonar picked up the image of 'a large moving target' following! Was Nessie looking for a friend?

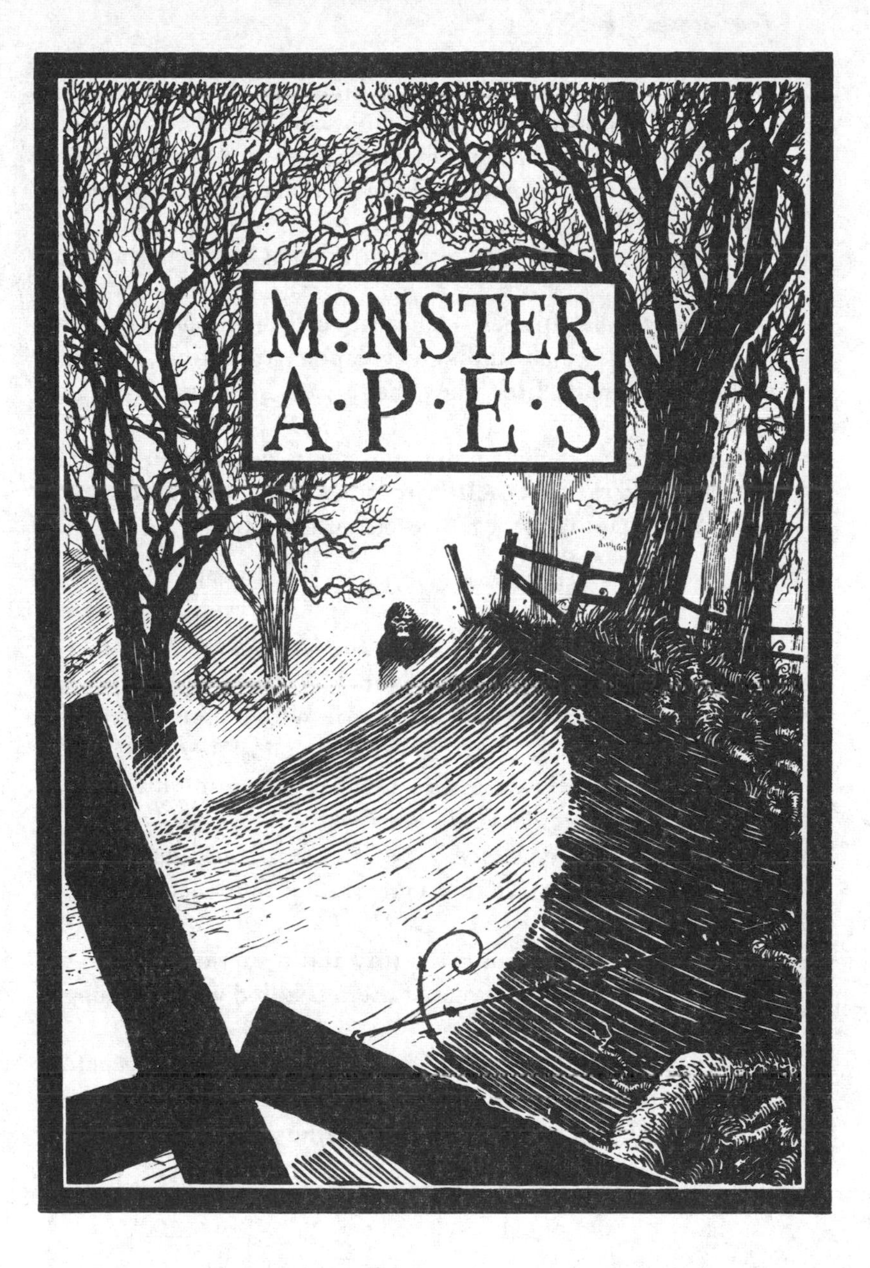
MONSTER
A·P·E·S

Nine million years ago a breed of giant ape roamed the plains and forests of southern Asia. For eight-and-a-half million years they survived the hardships of weather and wild animals. Then, just half a million years ago there came another, smaller ape that drove them to extinction.

The old giant apes — scientists call them *Gigantopithecus* – had strength.

The new, smaller apes – scientists call them *Homo Erectus* – had brains. They made tools and weapons from stone, bone and wood. They made fire. They made *you*. They were the first humans.

Humans used their cunning and their weapons to take the best food and the best shelter from the giant apes. So the giant apes, old Gigantopithecus, died out. Or did they . . .?

The Yeti

Lhakpa Sherpani was cold. Even in the summer months it is cold in the Himalayan mountains of Nepal. But she huddled into her goatskin jacket and prodded the cattle with a pointed stick.

"Lhakpa! Take the cattle up the mountain," her mother had ordered. "But make sure they're back before nightfall! You don't want any accidents, do you?"

Lhakpa had pulled a face. "No, Mother." She was a big girl now – nineteen years old this summer. She didn't need to be told to be careful.

"And don't let the animals stray too near the ledges," the woman had gone on. "If one of them is killed we'll go hungry this winter!"

"No, mother," she sighed as she stretched sleepily before going to collect the four Tibetan cattle, the yak, from the pen.

Now the fat, slow yak lumbered up the path and swung their long-horned heads from side to side in time with their plodding pace.

After an hour's climb the girl stopped and let her cattle graze just below the snow-line of the mountain. She sat with her back to a rock. It sheltered her from the wind that always moaned through the mountains. The sun was warm on her tanned face. She ate a little of the cheese and bread her mother had packed, then leaned back and looked lazily down the valley.

The sun on the distant mountains dazzled her and she closed her brown eyes to rest. Slowly she slipped into a shallow sleep. She hardly knew she'd dozed off when she opened her eyes with a start. Something had wakened her. She didn't know what.

The wind had whipped a cloud around the mountain as she slept. The thin mist crawled down her neck.

But that wasn't what had awakened her. She jumped to her feet nervously. The yak! They were huddled together and moving up the mountain at a trot. It was as if they were running away from something.

Lhakpa called them but they swerved away with frightened bellows. Suddenly, from the corner of her eye she saw something moving behind a boulder. An arm. An arm waving to the yak and driving them towards the edge of a steep cliff where they would be cornered.

The girl gasped as the creature jumped out from behind the rock and raced after the terrified animals. Lhakpa had never seen such a creature before but she knew at once what it was. She'd heard the village stories since she was a tiny child.

"Yeti!" she cried.

But she hadn't time to think of what the monster might do to her. All she was thinking of was her mother's warning. If she lost an animal then the family would go hungry that winter.

The creature was well under two metres tall but twice as wide as the girl. It grabbed the first yak by the horns and twisted. The yak screamed and fell in a tangled heap. Its neck was broken.

"No-o-o!" Lhakpa screamed and the creature turned to face her. Its hair was thick and black below the waist, more a golden brown above it. The Yeti's fingers were thick, with nails like claws. The monster's face was almost human.

It ignored the girl and went after a second yak which it wrestled down with a single twist of its huge arms. At last Lhakpa reached the Yeti and thrashed wildly with her fists against the body – as solid as Everest itself.

The creature snorted and waved a hand at her as if swatting a fly. It caught the mountain girl on the jaw and sent her tumbling down the mountain slope.

This time it took her longer to awake. When she did her jaw felt broken and her sight was blurred. The sun was low in an amber sky and the freezing night was sliding over the mountains.

She stumbled back to the village with her tale of horror. At first all she could say through her swollen mouth was, "Yeti! Yeti!"

Her mother smoothed her hair gently and wiped her face with a damp cloth. Her father raged, "She fell asleep again! Tell the truth, girl, you fell asleep again! The yak went over the ledge! Isn't that right?"

"Yeti! Yeti!" she moaned.

No one wanted to search the mountain that night. But at first light the next day the villagers gathered sticks and knives and set off grimly up the path to the grazing grounds.

They found no Yeti. But they found five dead yak, and one had had its throat torn out by something with terrible claws. The rest had had their necks broken by something with terrible strength.

Lhakpa's father stared at the white wilderness above the snowline. At the rocks and ravines, the cliffs and the mist-shrouded snowfields that could hide an army of monsters. He nodded. "Sorry, Lhakpa," he muttered to himself. "You were right. Yeti."

Yeti – FACT FILE

1. Yeti are often called 'Abominable Snowmen' because they live above the snow-line of the Himalayas, but most reports agree that they are brown in colour, not white like a snowman.

2. 'Yeti' is a Tibetan word meaning 'dweller among the high rocks.'

3. A Chinese book written in the 1700s has drawings of Tibetan wildlife. It includes a picture of a heavy, hairy, human-like creature. The head comes to a furry point, the face is whitish with deep-sunken, red eyes and its arms dangle almost to its knees.

4. There have been more sightings of Yeti footprints than of the creature itself. It has wide, five-toed feet which some say could be from a langur monkey. Others believe that the sightings have been of yellow snow-bears.

5. The world's highest mountain is Mount Everest in the heart of Yeti country. The first man to climb that mountain was Sir Edmund Hillary in 1953. Seven years later he returned to the Himalayas at the head of an expedition to find the famous Yeti. He didn't find one. But Yeti scalps were said to be held by Tibetan monasteries. Sir Edmund brought one back. Scientists examined it. The 'scalp' turned out to be an old monk's hat made from goatskin!

6. No remains of anything like a complete Yeti have ever been found, though part of a mummified hand was found at Pangboche, Nepal, in the 1950s. It was described by some zoologists as 'almost human' and 'similar in some respects to that of Neanderthal man.'

7. There are no reports of Yeti carrying off humans – but there are reports of unexplained disappearances in the Sikkim region of the Himalayas where no traces have ever been found. A Norwegian uranium prospector, Jan Frostis, did claim that in 1948, he was attacked and his shoulder badly mauled by a Yeti he met near Zemu Gap in Sikkim.

8. A Tibetan story tells how a Yeti once slept on the roof of a yak-herder's hut at night to enjoy the warmth from the fire. The terrified herder put yak dung on the fire and smoked the Yeti away!

9. Sir Tashi, the religious leader of a Tibetan province, used to claim that the Yeti would come and see him on the 29th of each month. If the Yeti pushed Sir Tashi then the man would quietly say, "Come now, that's enough of that," and the creature would leave.

10. While the Tibetans have known about the Yeti for hundreds of years the first outsider to see footprint evidence was the British explorer, Major Waddell, in 1889. The first British resident in Nepal, B. H. Hodgson, described a creature he'd never seen before which "moved erectly, was covered in long, dark hair and had no tail."

Sasquatch

Monsters have feelings too. At least they do if we believe Albert Ostman's incredible story. Albert Ostman was a lumberjack working in British Columbia which later became known for its huge ape man called Bigfoot in the United States and Sasquatch over the border in Canada. Albert was camping out in the forest one night when he was suddenly picked up and carried off by a very strange creature. When this story happened in 1924 Mr Ostman didn't tell many about his amazing experience. Those he did tell thought that he was mad! He said no more about it for thirty-three years. Then, in 1957, stories were published about a monster ape in north-west America. It was given the name of a native American legend – Sasquatch.

This persuaded Ostman to break his silence. He took an oath before a Justice of the Peace that the story was true. People who heard Mr Ostman tell this story, believe it. He died some years later still swearing that this account is correct in every detail. Read his own words and make up your mind.

"I was inside my sleeping bag and being carried like a sack of potatoes. The only thing in sight was a huge hand clutching the neck of the bag. It was a rough journey, and it seemed to go on forever, but I guess it was about three hours. Finally he stopped and let me down. Then he dropped my packsack, I could hear the cans rattle. Then I heard some chatter – some kind of talk I didn't understand.

The ground was sloping so when he let go of my sleeping bag I rolled over head first downhill. I got my head out and got some air. I tried to straighten my legs and crawl out, but my legs were numb. It was still dark. I couldn't see what my captors looked like. I tried to massage my legs to get some life in them and get my shoes on.

I could hear now it was at least four of them. They were standing round me chattering non-stop. I knew then that I was with the Sasquatch.

As it grew lighter I could make them out. Four of them all right. Big and covered in short thick hair. Seemed to be two parents and two youngsters, a boy and a girl. The young fellow must have been eleven to eighteen years old but he was way over two metres tall. He had wide jaws, narrow forehead.

The old lady was even taller than the boy. She was not built for beauty or for speed. The man's eye teeth were longer than the rest of his teeth, but not long enough to be called tusks. The old man must have been two-and-a-half metres tall. Big barrel chest and a hump on his back. His finger-nails were like chisels. The soles of their feet seemed to be padded like a dog's foot and the big toe was longer than the rest and very strong.

They didn't seem to want to harm me so I decided to stay where I was till I could figure out a way to escape. I had some food, ammunition for the rifle, a knife, a few matches and some snuff. Didn't realize how useful that snuff was going to be.

They let me prepare my own food from the tins I had. But next day when I tried to leave the old man pushed me back. Seemed he and the girl were keeping a close watch on me. The old lady and the boy did the food collecting and housekeeping. They came home with arms full of grass and twigs as well as some kind of nuts that grow in the ground. The young fellow picked some kind of grass with long sweet roots. He gave me some one day. They tasted very sweet.

As the days went by I figured what they wanted me for. They wanted me for the young girl. Either as a pet . . . or as a mate! I knew then I had to escape. At the same time I didn't want to shoot my way out unless I had to.

The way I came to escape came through a lucky chance.

I discovered that the young fellow had a liking for my snuff. I waited for him and the old lady to go off on their errands into the forest. I thought I might be able to give the old man a taste of it while he was guarding me. Maybe throw it in his face or give him too much and choke him.

He watched me taking some. He came closer. I held the box towards him. Before I could throw it he snatched the whole box out of my hand. He swallowed it all in one. Not even a Sasquatch can take that!

After a few minutes his eyes began to roll over in his head and he was looking straight up. I could see he was sick. Then he grabbed my coffee can that was quite cold by this time. He emptied it into his mouth, grounds and all. That did no good.

He stuck his head between his legs and rolled forward a few times away from me. Then he began to squeal like a stuck pig. I grabbed my rifle. I said to myself, "This is it. If he comes for me I'll shoot him plumb between the eyes."

But he started for the spring. He wanted water. I packed my sleeping bag in my packsack with the few cans I had left.

That was when the young fellow came back and spotted me. He ran over to his mother. Then she began to squeal. I started for the opening in the wall – and I just made it. The old lady was right behind me. I fired one shot at the rock above her head. That frightened her enough to let me escape.

I must have run three miles in record time till I came to a logging camp and civilization once again."

Sasquatch – FACT FILE

1. Sasquatch does not like dogs. There are many reports of dogs being given a serious beating by the ape man.

2. Sasquatch does not appear to like baths either. His smell has been described as "like a skunk" or "like rotting flesh".

3. Sightings of Sasquatch have been linked with sightings of UFOs (Unidentified Flying Objects) and one idea is that Sasquatch is an alien. The first sighting of a footprint by a European was in 1811 when the explorer and trader, David Thompson, came across a whole trail of gigantic prints. He measured them at 35 cm long by 20 cm wide.

4. Most early sightings of Sasquatch were in the north-west United States. In some parts of the United States a similar monster is known as Bigfoot. In this part of the world there are thousands of square kilometres of mountain forests and few roads or towns, the ideal spot for a giant ape to live without being seen for years.

5. Some people believe that Sasquatch could be related to Yeti. They think Yeti could have crossed from Asia to America thousands of years ago when the two continents were joined by a land-bridge. However, they do not explain how the huge Yowie has been seen so much – for the Yowie lives in Australia!

6. In 1884 a young Sasquatch was seen from a train travelling through British Columbia (west Canada). The crew stopped the train and captured it. They named it Jacko and after going on show in the county it was sold to a circus. Jacko was a pretty small Sasquatch. Some experts believe he could have been a runaway chimpanzee.

7. In 1967 two men succeeded in capturing Bigfoot on about 6 metres of movie film. The film shows what could be a man in a gorilla skin – or what could be a real monster. If it is a fake then it's a very good one – people are still arguing about it. One scientist who has studied the film in minute detail still won't say it's a fake or a genuine film. All he will say is, "I couldn't see the zipper, and I still can't."

8. Sasquatch has been given the blame for some pretty nasty crimes. In 1910 the McLeod brothers went mining in the Nahanni Valley in the North West Territories of Canada. They were found with their heads cut off. Sasquatch was reported to have been seen in the area and was given the blame. The place became known as Headless Valley.

9. Bigfoot means big business in the United States. You can go on Bigfoot expeditions, stay in the Bigfoot Motel and eat Bigfoot burgers. But you can't shoot Bigfoot – at least not in California where it is a protected species.

10. If a Sasquatch comes to your door, beware! It has been said it has the power to hypnotize you, or to trick you with its voice (like a ventriloquist). You should be able to recognize one because witnesses say their eyes glow red . . . or orange . . . or green – depending on which you choose to believe!

The Yowie of Australia

The Aborigines knew all about the hairy giant long before Europeans came to Australia. They had many names for the creature, but now it is generally called the Yowie. Australia has thousands of acres of bushland rarely visited by humans. It would be easy for a family of creatures to stay undiscovered for years.

But, as the settlers spread across the continent, sightings of an ape man began to be recorded. One, seen by Johnnie McWilliams in 1894, seemed a little less tough than the average monster.

Johnnie was on his way from his home in Snowball to the Jinden Post Office in New South Wales, when he saw "a big man covered with long hair." The Yowie was as shocked as Johnnie by the meeting and ran off across open country before disappearing over a hill. But the creature made a mistake – it kept its eyes on the boy as it ran, and didn't look where it was going. As a result it caught its foot against a log and gave a bellow of pain.

One of the clearest sightings was in 1912, also in New South Wales. Charles Harper was a Sydney surveyor who was camping with friends in the Currickbilly Mountains. Hearing a noise in the dark they threw some kindling on the fire and it flared up to give them a better look at the intruder. Charles Harper described it as . . .

"A huge man-like animal. It stood erect, not twenty metres from the fire, growling, grimacing, and thumping his breast with his huge hand-like paws. I looked round and saw one of my companions had fainted. He remained unconscious for some hours. The creature stood in one position for some time, sufficiently long to enable me to photograph him on my brain.

I should say its height when standing erect would be 5ft 8in to 5ft 10in [1.73 to 1.78 metres]. Its body, legs and arms were covered with long, brownish-red hair, which shook with every quivering movement of its body. The hair on its shoulder and back parts appeared in the subdued light of the fire to be jet black and long; but what struck me as extraordinary was the apparently human shape, but still so very different.

I will commence its detailed description with the feet, which only occasionally I could get a glimpse of. I saw that the metatarsal [foot] bones were very short, much shorter than in a human, but the toes were extremely long, indicating great grasping power in the feet. The shin-bone of the leg was much shorter than in a human. The thigh-bone was very long, out of proportion to the rest of the leg. The body frame was enormous, indicating immense strength and power of endurance. The arms and forepaws were extremely long and large, and very muscular, being covered with shorter hair. The head and face were very small, but very human. The eyes were large, dark and piercing, deeply set. A most horrible mouth was ornamented with two large and long canine teeth. When the jaws were closed they protruded over the lower lip. The stomach seemed like a sack hanging halfway down to the thighs. All this observation occupied a few minutes while the creature stood erect as if the firelight had paralysed him.

After a few more growls and thumping his breast he made off, the first few yards erect, then at a faster gait on all fours through the low scrub. Nothing would induce my companions to continue the trip, at which I was rather pleased, and returned as quickly as possible out of reach of the Australian gorillas, rare as they are."

The Yowie – FACT FILE

1. Australian Yowie researcher, Rex Gilroy, has collected over 3000 reports of Yowie sightings.

2. The Yowie has a lot in common with its Yeti and Bigfoot Sasquatch cousins: not only its size and its hairiness but its sickening smell too. One witness described it as being "like a public lavatory."

3. A Yowie was shot in the Brindabella Mountains in New South Wales, but not killed. The Webb brothers, Joseph and William, saw one approach their camp at the turn of this century. When it refused to stop they took aim and fired, but the bullet failed to have any effect other than scaring the Yowie away. Reports of encounters with Sasquatch have suggested that it too is unhurt by bullets.

4. Yowies are curious. They are reported watching humans at work, not interfering, but not afraid.

5. Yowies, like Yeti, have been known to attack humans. In 1968 in a saw-milling settlement of Kookaburra, New South Wales, George Grey woke to find a greasy, hairy ape man on top of him. This one was only about 1.20 metres tall, so he was able to throw it off after a struggle, and run away.

6. Like Sasquatch the reported sightings of Yowies increased in the 1970s.

7. A footprint left by a Yowie in 1912 showed only four toes.

8. One bold Yowie is said to have put its head around a door in Springbrook on the Gold Coast and stayed until someone threw a chair at it.

9. Some scientists argue against the possibility of Yowies existing, saying it doesn't make sense. The Yowie's description would make it a Primate (highest form of mammal, e.g. man, ape) – but the first and only Primates in Australia are human beings, and they arrived in boats. Every native Australian mammal is a marsupial (mammals with pouches, e.g. kangaroo).

10. Yowies make a sound like a pig's grunt. When upset they can roar like a bull.

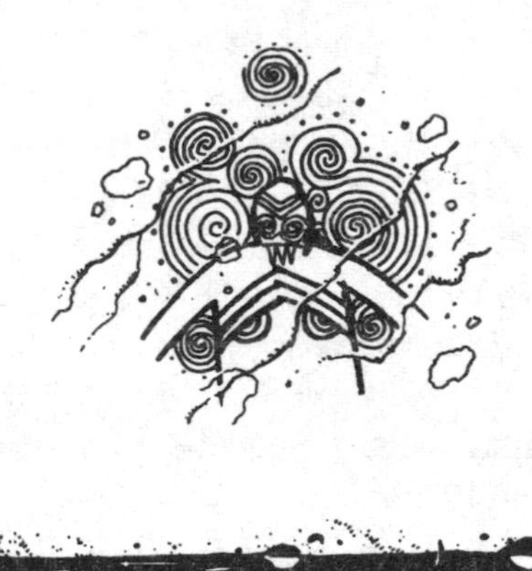

PHANTOM
ANIMALS

"The moon was shining bright upon the clearing, and there in the centre lay the unhappy maid where she had fallen, dead of fear and fatigue. But it was not the sight of her body, nor was it that of Hugo Baskerville lying near her, which raised the hair upon the heads of those three men. But it was that, standing over Hugo, and plucking at his throat, there stood a foul thing, a great black beast, shaped like a hound, yet larger than any hound that ever mortal eye has rested upon. And even as they looked the thing tore the throat out of Hugo Baskerville. As it turned its blazing eyes and dripping jaws upon them, the three shrieked with fear and rode for dear life, still screaming across the moor. One, it is said, died that very night of what he had seen, and the other two were broken men for the rest of their days."

The Hound of The Baskervilles by Sir Arthur Conan Doyle

Of course the great Sherlock Holmes didn't believe in monstrous Black Dogs. After a couple of murders he discovers that the hound is just a big vicious dog, half starved so it will kill, and painted in luminous liquid to glow in the dark and scare its victims into the nasty bog known as Grimpen Mire.

It's a great story. Not a word of it is true. But Conan Doyle didn't make up all the elements of the story. For the legend of a great hound has been passed down for hundreds of years. Some stories are in the imagination of frightened people – people walking along country roads at night before street lighting was thought of. Strange scufflings in the hedgerows, the snort of a curious cow as it poked its head over a wall. The barking foxes in the forest, the screech of a creature caught by an owl. Enough to make anyone imagine they were being chased by a nightmare hound.

But some stories are not so easily explained. Some even have evidence. If you want to find the great Black Dog then England is probably the best place, though they have been reported all over the world, and, while most English counties have their stories, the county of Suffolk seems to be the home of the beast.

And in Suffolk the most likely place would be the peaceful village of Blythburgh . . .

The Black Dog of Blythburgh

The land around Blythburgh is flat. Some time in the distant past it struggled up out of the sea. But now the sea is slowly taking it back.

Just down the coast the waves are eating into the soft cliffs. One by one the villages have slid into those waves. They say that on a stormy night you can hear the church bells chiming from one sea-swallowed village. Dunwich it was called. A ghost village now.

A couple of miles inland, over rugged heath and forest, stands a church. Taller and grander than most country churches, it looks out over the deep, dark marshes. It is Blythburgh Church, known as the Cathedral of the Marshes.

Even today it is peaceful in summer, lonely when the cold winds whip off the North Sea . . . and menacing when it begins to grow dark. When eerie sounds echo over the marshes; when old tales of monster dogs become believable. When you can understand the terror that gripped the folk of Blythburgh four hundred years ago.

Sunday 4 August 1577

It began in Bungay village church just seven miles away. The Suffolk sky is vast at any time – no hills to shorten the horizon. That day it towered over the countryside with great grey menacing clouds. The distant rumbles warned the people of a storm to come. They hurried for the shelter of the church, little knowing that there was no safety there. The storm hurried nearer. Then it broke above the churches: the one in Bungay and the one in Blythburgh. Abraham Fleming was in Bungay church that day and told what happened next . . .

"Immediately hereupon there appeared to the congregation a horrible likeness of a dog, black in colour. At the sight of the dog, and of the fearful flashes that were there seen, many of the people believed that Doomsday was already come.

This black dog (or the devil in the likeness of a dog) ran along down the body of the church with great swiftness and incredible haste. It ran among the people in a visible form and shape and passed between two persons as they were kneeling upon their knees, seemingly in prayer. It wrung the necks of them both at one instant. Clean backwards, so far that in a moment, as they kneeled, they strangely died.

There was at the same time another wonder wrought. For the same dog, remaining in the same shape and form, passed by another man in the congregation. He gave him such a bite on the back that the man was soon drawn together and shrunk up, like a piece of leather scorched in a hot fire; or like the mouth of a purse drawn together with a string.

That man, although he was so strangely attacked, died not, but is thought as yet alive. That is marvellous in the eyes of men and an amazing thing to the mind."

But the Black Dog hadn't finished yet. He hurried to the church at Blythburgh, seven miles away, and caused similar chaos . . .

"Placing himself upon the main roof beam suddenly he swung down through the church. There, as before, he slew two men and a lad. He burned the hand of another person that was there among the rest of the company of whom several were blasted."

Abraham Fleming was the pastor of a London church. An honest man?

In Bungay market place today they have a weather vane, but instead of the usual cockerel they have the image of a leaping Black Dog.

And what has Blythburgh Church to show? Look closely at the main front door. There you'll see some black scorch marks. They say the Black Dog left them as he raced into the church.

Monster Black Dogs – FACT FILE

1. Black Dog monsters have been reported all over Europe, North and South America but their origins seem to be the British Isles. One is reported as early as 1127 in the *Anglo-Saxon Chronicle*. A pack of Black Dogs kept the monks of Peterborough awake from Lent until Easter as they hunted the fens of East Anglia. They were led by a huntsman dressed in jet black.

2. You can tell a monster Black Dog from a normal dog by its size and its eyes. They are often very large – "as tall as a mantelpiece" – and have eyes, large as saucers, that glow. In fact the Black Dog of Winsford Hill in Somerset is said to fade slowly until only the glowing eyes are left. The Kludde of Belgium is easier to spot because it is a huge Black Dog with wings that walks on its hind legs; it also makes the sound of a clanking chain. It uses the chain to beat its victims. It is no use trying to outrun the Kludde. The faster you run the faster it follows, slithering between trees like a giant snake.

3. Black Dog monsters don't often make much noise. Their footsteps are silent and they rarely bark. But when they do make a noise it is odd: footsteps like the clopping of a horse, a blood-chilling howl or even a devilish laugh. Be particularly careful of the ones that talk. A man met one on the road to Woolpit in Suffolk which said to him, "I shall want you within the week!"

. . . and he died the next night. A similar dog was said to roam the graveyards of Chicago in the 1940s. But it was white. To see the White Dog meant certain death within the year.

4. In the north of England the Black Dog is known as Trash, Skryker or the Barguest. In East Anglia it is Shuck, Scarfe or Skeff. Hooter is its name in Midland England and Hairy Jack in Lincolnshire. The Irish call their Black Dog, Pooka.

5. If you try to pat a monster Black Dog you may find that your hand goes right through it. However some people report that the dog vanishes if you try to stroke it. However, a man tried to stroke a Black Dog which blocked his road at Hatfield Peverell, Essex, in 1850. He clearly believed that it was a normal dog. He was burnt to ashes along with his horse and cart.

6. The Black Dog sometimes appears with an unusual head: the head of a monk (Clopton Hall near Great Bealings, Suffolk), the head of an ape (Balsham and West Wratting in Suffolk), or sometimes with no head at all.

7. Black Dogs don't seem to have a lot of road sense. There are several reports of motorists running "into" Black Dogs as they dash across the road. However, when the motorist gets out to see if the animal is hurt, it has vanished.

8. Real pet dogs and police dogs are reported to be terrified in the presence of the monster Black Dogs. Two police dogs got into a fight with an invisible Black Dog in France in 1939. The battle lasted two minutes and ended with the death of one of the police dogs.

9. Black Dogs are often seen near water (as with the case in Blythburgh Marshes), near churches and near crossroads.

10. In the 1950s a Black Dog terrorized the area of Kettleness near Whitby. Strangely in Bram Stoker's story, *Dracula*, the writer described the vampire coming ashore at Kettleness . . . in the form of a huge hound!

Some monster animals, like the Black Dogs, are clearly known animals. But known animals become mysterious when they appear – and disappear – in the wrong places at the wrong times. They can behave with great ferocity and terrorize a community. One such animal is the kangaroo. Common enough in the outback of Australia – monstrous in the towns and cities of twentieth-century America . . .

The Phantom Kangaroo

"Granny, can I go out to play?" the girl asked.

The woman looked up sharply from her sewing. Then she glanced at the window. "It's getting a little dark, Lucy. Best not go outside now."

The woman poked the fire until the log crackled and flared, then returned to her sewing.

Pouting Lucy flung herself into an armchair. "Mom lets me go out at this time. It's only six o'clock."

"Your mom's left me in charge. She'd never forgive me if something happened to you," Granny explained.

The girl wriggled and scowled. "Why can't I go out, Granny?"

The woman put down her sewing and leaned forward in her chair. "Lucy, it isn't safe to go out on the streets after dark."

"Why?"

Granny sighed and looked over the top of her spectacles at the girl. "Someone or something might get you."

"What thing, Granny?" Lucy asked with a nervous laugh.

The woman's eyes shifted to the flickering shadows in the corner of the room and she whispered, "The kangaroo!"

Now Lucy's laugh was scornful. "Kangaroo! Kangaroo! Oh, come on, you're not trying to tell me there's a nasty kangaroo out there waiting to get me? Even Mom never tries that sort of story on me."

But Granny didn't laugh. "Your mom wasn't born when the great kangaroo scare hit America. But I was. I was just about your age."

"Kangaroo scare? People were scared of a kangaroo! Were you scared of it?" Lucy giggled.

Granny looked into the amber flames and shook her head. "Older and wiser people than I were scared of the phantom kangaroo. Priests and policemen and tough old truck drivers were scared of him. I was just plain terrified."

Lucy shuffled foward onto the edge of her seat. "Tell me about it, Gran."

"It started in South Pittsburg, Tennessee, not far from where I was brought up. My pa came in all excited one night and read the newspaper report to us kids. It was some time in January 1934. The Reverend W. J. Handcock saw the beast in a field and described it to the newspaper. I remember Pa reading that report clear as yesterday. 'It was fast as lightning and looked like a giant kangaroo running and leaping across the field.' Then it went on to tell of a large dog being killed . . ."

"Could have been run down by a truck," Lucy objected.

Granny shook her head. "The dog was killed . . . and eaten. So were lots of chickens in the nearby farms!"

"Did they catch it?" Lucy asked eagerly.

"The police took the Reverend seriously – him being a minister and all – and they had a big search for the beast. They never found a thing."

"You reckon the priest was lying?" Lucy asked, a little shocked.

Granny shrugged. "If he was, then so were lots of others. Someone came up with the story that they'd seen the kangaroo escaping from a farm with a dead sheep tucked underneath each arm."

Lucy shuddered. "And they never saw it again?"

"Not for fifteen years. I remember I'd just finished college that year when that old kangaroo turned up again. This time it was up at Grove City, Ohio. A driver saw something hop across the beams of his headlights as he drove along at night."

Lucy squinted at her grandmother. "Are you sure you're telling me the truth?"

The woman rose stiffly from her chair and went to the old dresser by the kitchen door. She sifted through some old papers until she came to a scrap-book filled with faded photos and newspaper cuttings. She sat on the arm of Lucy's chair and pointed out the pages. "I was interested in the story, seeing the first had happened so near where I was a girl. I kept some of the cuttings. Here we are. The driver was Louis Staub . . ."

Lucy read on, " 'It was about five-and-a-half feet [1.68 metres] high, hairy and brownish. It had a pointed head. It looked like a kangaroo but it appeared to jump on all fours. I'm certain it wasn't a deer.' " The girl looked up. "Maybe it *was* a kangaroo! Maybe it escaped from the local zoo!"

"They thought of that. None were ever reported missing. Same as when children kept reporting a 'big bunny' they saw in Coon Rapids, Minnesota."

The girl frowned at the fire. "That was still way before I was born. If I go out to play there sure won't be any kangaroo waiting to tuck me under his hairy old arm."

Her grandmother said nothing. She simply turned the page to some more newspaper cuttings. These were not so yellowed with age.

" 'Eighteenth of October, 1974,' " Lucy read. " 'Chicago!' "

"That's right. A man called the police and said there was a kangaroo hopping around his front porch. The police didn't believe it of course, but they had to send a couple of patrol men out to investigate. And what do you think they found when they got there?"

Lucy's eyes were wide and her mouth slightly open. "What?"

"A kangaroo, of course!"

"Did they shoot it?" the girl gasped.

"No. They didn't have the heart. They chased it into a back alley and tried to catch it. But it started lashing out, the way they do, with those big back legs, and the police backed off. In the end it hopped over a fence and escaped. They had lots of reports from people claiming they'd seen a kangaroo rummaging through their garbage bins. One newspaper boy even claimed it hopped up to him and stared. The newspapers had a great time of it."

The woman pointed to a headline and Lucy giggled as she read it out loud. " 'KANGAROO STAYS A JUMP AHEAD OF THE POLICE.' "

"There were more reports from towns to the west of Chicago – here's one from Plano, Illinois. Three young men driving along and one says, 'We almost ran over it. It jumped onto the road about twenty feet [6.1 metres] ahead of us . . . it landed on the road near the junction with the main road and there was no traffic. It sat up on its haunches and then jumped over a fence about five feet high [1.52 metres] and disappeared into the woods.' "

Lucy turned the page. "A few smaller reports from 1976 . . . Wisconsin . . .Colorado . . . Ohio. Wow! It sure gets around."

Her granny smiled and closed the book. "It could be anywhere, any time. It could be out there right now, waiting for some little girl to poke her nose out of the door. Then he'll just tuck her under his arm and hop off into the night."

The girl shivered and wriggled closer to the fire. She glanced towards the windows that showed the purple velvet sky closing in. Her grandmother closed the curtains and threw another log on the fire.

"It's getting a little cold out there," Lucy said softly. "Perhaps I'll just stay in and read a book."

Granny smiled and went back to her sewing.

Monster Phantom Animals – FACT FILE

1. Mysterious cats are almost as common as dogs. They are reported all over the world. They are blamed for savaging farm animals but are rarely caught or photographed. Zoos never admit to losing animals at the time of their appearance.

2. There are no reports of phantom kangaroos in Australia. However they do have the famous Bunyip that inhabits lakes or swamps and drags its victims down to their deaths. There are countless Bunyip stories – some refer to known animals, some to mythical beasts, but many to an unidentified monster. Twentieth-century reports are rare so it may now be extinct. It may have been a fresh-water seal . . . but they have only been known in Canada and parts of Asia. Aborigines thought of the Bunyip as a *demon* or a *spirit* and this is the most likely truth. The Bunyip is just a monster of legend.

3. A curious mongoose attracted a lot of publicity on the Isle of Man in 1931. It lived with the Irving family and thirteen-year-old Voirrey Irving taught it to talk. It declared its name was Gef. Several investigators heard it chatting away behind the panelled walls of the Irvings' farmhouse – but no one, except Voirrey, ever saw it. Was Gef a phantom mongoose . . . or the creation of a lonely teenage girl with a talent for ventriloquism?

4. A mysterious animal left a hundred miles of footprints in the snow. It happened in Devon in February 1855. The prints in the shape of a horse's hoof ran over roofs, crossed a river, appeared to enter and exit a drain-pipe and to leap over a 4-metre wall. In many places they stopped suddenly as if the creature had risen into the air. The explanations over the years have included badgers, cats, foxes, otters, cranes, donkeys, a pony with a broken shoe, rats, rabbits, squirrels and even toads. Of course an escaped kangaroo has been suggested. The most popular explanation at the time was that it was the Devil himself who had walked through Devon that night.

5. The Griffin was generally accepted as a purely imaginary beast: the body of a lion with the head and wings of an eagle. But in 1984 there were several sightings of such a creature in Brentford in London. It was said to be the size of a large dog and flew with a very slow flapping of its wings. Curiously the coat of arms of Brentford District Council shows two griffins supporting a shield . . . and Brentford Football club play at Griffin Park.

6. A vicious phantom monkey was commonly seen on a bridge over the Birmingham and Liverpool canal in the late 1870s. It scared horses and riders, but attempts to whip it failed when the whip passed straight through it. After one attack on 21 January 1879 the policeman investigating shrugged off the complaint with the

comment, "Oh, is that all, sir? I know what that was. That was the man-monkey, sir, as does come again at that bridge ever since the man was drowned in the canal."

S·E·A
MONSTERS

Monsters seem to have lurked in the seas since the dawn of time. Sailors forced to stay at home on winter nights must have made up tales to thrill the children.

Fishermen today still tell tales of monstrous fish that they once caught . . . but in the struggle 'got away'. And every time the tale is told the fish grows slightly bigger. Was that how the legends of Ancient Greece began, with sailors returning and exaggerating their encounters with large fish or sea mammals?

But stories of *true* sea-monsters are hard to find before 1550 . . . and even then they are suspiciously unreal.

Olaus Magnus described one in the year of 1555. The monster had a large square head, with two great horns, and huge eyes. The creature could be seen at night because it glowed a firey red.

Again in 1555 a giant squid was washed ashore along the Iceland coast. The tentacles were missing, but still it measured 18 metres. With its tentacles it would have measured a monstrous 30 metres, maybe more. These are often said to be the first reports of some true ocean giants.

But a well-recorded, and most reliable, early report comes from the ambassador to Venice, no less. After a visit to England back in 1532 he sent this report back to his senate . . .

"In the month of August this sea of ours stranded near Tynemouth a dead animal of exceeding great size, which for the most part has been already pulled apart; and what remains is of such bulk that 100 wains [wagons] could scarcely carry it away.

Those who first saw this animal, and described it as precisely as they could, say it measured 30 yards or 90 feet [28 metres]; from the belly to the fin on the back, which was buried in the sand, the length was eight or nine yards [8 metres].

The exact dimensions cannot be ascertained because, when I went to see this animal on 27 August, it emitted such a stench as to be almost unbearable; but its back, covered by the sand, is some three yards broad [2.7 metres] so that the sea beats upon it daily and the waves break over it. The opening of the mouth is 6½ yards [6 metres]; the length of each jaw 7½ yards [7 metres]. Altogether it is as big as a large oak.

It has thirty ribs on its sides, and for the most part they are 21 feet long [6.5 metres] and one half foot [15 centimetres] in diameter.

It has three bellies like very large caves, and thirty throats, five of which are larger than the rest; it has two wings or fins for swimming, each of which is 15 feet long [4.5 metres] so that ten oxen could scarcely draw one of them away. Adhering to the palate were certain horny *laminae* [thin, bony plates] having on one side in number upwards of 1000, one of which I send thee. It is not a lie, Polydore, but a thing perfectly true, though they are not all of one size.

The length from the beginning of the head to the aperture of the mouth is 7 yards [6.5 metres]. Concerning the tongue some persons differ; the majority say that it was 7 yards long [6.5 metres].

A certain man having entered the body to pull it to pieces, fell, and would have

81

been drowned had he not clung to a rib.

The space between the eyes is 6 yards [5.5 metres] and the nostrils are very disproportioned to so huge a frame for they resemble those of an ox. The tail is forked and notched like a saw.

In its head were two large holes from which it is supposed to spout forth water as if by tubes. It had no teeth, so people guess that it is not a whale, as whales have very large teeth; but in its mouth were the horny *laminae* mentioned above."

A true monster – even the largest fish today (a whale shark) is only half that length. If it wasn't an unknown monster then it could only have been a blue whale – the largest and heaviest creature of all time. The largest weigh as much as 3135 average men – that's more than enough to fill those thirty wagons! Blue whales have been hunted almost to extinction by man. But, back in 1532, they could just have grown that big.

The more men sailed the seas, the stranger were the things they saw. And the stranger their tales became of giant squids that sank their ships, and mermaids combing out their hair.

Mr Cobbin of Durban saw a beast from the boat *Silvery Wave* . . . he *said*. It had a head like a bull, a back covered in rainbow-coloured scales like armour and it raced through the water with a caterpillar wiggle. He claimed it was over 1000 yards (925 metres) long!

If we believe him then this beast was *ten times* larger than the blue whale and about three times as long as the Eiffel Tower is high. There have even been reports of a sea monster thirty metres long, the shape of a tadpole and striped black and yellow.

But some stories are more believable than others and need to be looked at more carefully. Stories like the case of Morgawr . . .

The Morgawr

The old Cornish man sat by the tavern fire and stared at the dancing flames. "Of course there's a monster out there in the bay," he chuckled. "Haven't you read the papers?"

The young man grinned. "I am the papers – at least I'm a reporter. Dave's the name. That's what I'm doing in Falmouth. I've come to follow up the stories about this funny fish."

The old man looked at him sharply and pointed his pipe stem at the reporter. "Don't go calling her no 'funny fish'. Her name's Morgawr."

"How do you spell that?" the young man asked.

"I didn't stop to ask her," the old man replied sourly.

"You've seen it too then?" the other asked eagerly. "I'm just off to meet a man who says he can conjure up this Morgawr with magic."

"That'll be the feller they call 'Doc' – not a proper doctor, of course. More like a witch-doctor."

"You don't believe it then?" Dave asked.

The man sucked on his pipe stem and shrugged. "Certainly lots of strange things seem to happen when he's around. You have to give him that. And not just Morgawr swimming around in Falmouth Bay."

"But you said you'd seen Morgawr yourself," Dave urged.

"Ahh! That was fifty years ago, back in 1926. We were out trawling when we caught her in the nets – twenty-foot (6.1 metres) long with an eight-foot (2.4 metres) tail. But it tore its way out of our nets with its huge beak!"

"A beak?" Dave laughed. He wasn't sure if the fisherman was making fun of him. But the old man looked serious enough. He fished inside his wallet for an old piece of newspaper. "Here's the report from the time – and one from 1876."

The young reporter peered at them carefully. The 1876 report was yellowed and wrinkled but Dave managed to read it.

West Briton Newspaper

" 'The Sea Serpent was caught alive in Gerrans Bay. Two of our fishermen were afloat, overhauling their crab pots about 400-500 yards [400 metres] from shore, when they discovered the serpent coiled about the floating cork [buoy]. Upon their near approach it lifted its head and showed signs of defiance, upon which they struck it forcibly with an oar, which so far disabled it as to allow them to proceed with their work, after which they observed the serpent floating about near their boat. They pursued it, bringing it ashore still alive for exhibition. Soon after which it was killed on the rocks and most inconsiderately cast again into the sea.' "

"But the monster was dead!" Dave objected.

The old man's watery blue eyes twinkled. "Maybe it had relatives. Fifty years later I saw it."

Dave nodded. "Fifty years, eh? And fifty years after that it pops up again."

"That's right," the fisherman agreed.

The reporter flipped through his notebook. "September 1975 – last year in fact – Mrs Scott of Falmouth saw a long-necked, hump-backed monster off Pendennis Point. It had horns and bristles on its neck. Let me see . . . reports over the winter . . . and then on 5 March the local paper and some photos from a woman calling herself Mary F."

"That's right. Looks like an elephant waving its trunk, except the trunk is its neck."

Dave shook his head. "But Mary F. never came forward and she said the negatives were sold to an American. Bit suspicious that. She doesn't name this mysterious American – almost as if she didn't want the negatives examined."

The fisherman lit his pipe with a spill from the fire. "Lots of other reports this summer, though. Respectable people too! Dentists, bankers from London, company directors."

"And witches," Dave grinned. "There's a report here of three girls coming down and swimming naked in the bay chanting magic spells!"

The old man chuckled. "Didn't put old Morgawr off though! She still kept appearing. That's when that Doc feller came down to investigate."

Dave glanced at his watch. "That reminds me. I'm meeting him on the Helford River bank in five minutes. Says he may be able to conjure up that fishy fraud for me!"

"Not a fish – a monster!" the old man reminded him.

Dave laughed as he stepped out into the raw November afternoon. "I'll believe it when I see it."

But Dave wasn't laughing when he returned to the inn that evening. The old fisherman was back at his fireside seat with a mug of ale and that smouldering pipe. Dave sat down heavily.

"Well? Did Doc introduce you to Morgawr?" the man asked.

The reporter shook his head, uncertain. "I'm not sure. I'll know when the film in my camera is developed."

"Morgawr let you take her picture then?"

And Dave told his story. He'd met the magician and begun to interview him. Then he'd taken some pictures of Doc waving a wand over the waves. All good entertaining stuff for the paper. "Doc wanted to take a few pictures of his own," Dave explained. "While I was waiting for him I kept warm by throwing some stones for my dog to chase. That's when Doc cried out that there was something out in the river – a dark head rising out of the water. I grabbed my camera and tried to fit a telephoto lens. But it was cold and I was fumbling with excitement."

"Morgawr has that effect on people," the old man nodded.

"But I made it in the end. I thought it was a seal's head, but then it raised itself up out of the water and the neck was too long and narrow for a seal."

"Sounds like the Morgawr I saw," the fisherman agreed. "What happened then?"

Dave looked sheepishly into his beer. "Then the dog started barking in the excitement – and Morgawr dived."

"So now you believe in the Sea Giant?"

"The what?"

"That's what Morgawr means in the old Cornish language – Sea Giant."

The young reporter stirred the fire with a stick and sighed. "I'll wait till I see the photos."

But Dave was disappointed. Just as with the Loch Ness Monster the camera was mysteriously faulty. The winder didn't work so the three photos came out on one jumbled frame. Doc's photos were taken without a telephoto lens and were too small to prove anything.

Dave was never sure what he'd seen.

The magician and monster-investigator, Doc Shiels, went on to take photos of the Loch Ness Monster the next year. So he's quite sure that unknown creatures of the sea still exist.

Many other people claim to have seen the Sea Giant and are ready to swear that monsters do exist in the sea.

And, of course, the old Cornish fishermen always believed in their Morgawr.

Sea Monsters – FACT FILE

1. In 1965 Dr Bernard Heuvelmans, a zoologist, looked at nearly 600 reported sightings of sea monsters. He decided there were nine types of sea monster:

Saurian – crocodile types;

Super Eel – snake-like but probably a fish;

Super Otter – a long-tailed mammal;

Many-finned – long, jointed mammal with triangular fins;

Many-humped – long mammal, blunt head, short neck, pair of flippers, humps along back;

Long-necked – a tailless seal type;

Seahorse – like the Long-necked but with large eyes, whiskers and a mane;

Giant Tadpole – yellow, tadpole-shaped, rarest sighting;

Giant Turtle – like the Archelon of the Mesozoic Era.

He decided that 358 sightings could not be explained as hoaxes, mistakes or confusion with known creatures and were therefore true.

2. One of the longest-lasting sea-monster legends concerns mermaids and mermen. A fish-tailed god is mentioned in the Bible. More recently South Africa's *Pretoria News* reported a mermaid sighting in a Lusaka storm-drain on 20 December 1977. The creature was "European woman from the waist up, whilst the rest of

her body was shaped like the back end of a fish, and covered with scales." Mermaid sightings are often explained as mistaken sea-mammals such as manatees and dugongs. But others believe that millions of years ago our human ancestors emerged from the seas to live on the land – merfolk are the ancestors who chose to stay in the sea.

3. In 1913 there was a report of a young sea monster off the coast of Australia. Oscar Davies, a Tasmanian State mining prospector, and his mate, W. Harris, saw it on the beach at sunset.

"It was fifteen feet [4.5m] long. It had a small head, a thick arched neck passing gradually into the barrel of the body. It had no definite tail and no fins. It was furred, the coat in appearance resembling that of a horse of a chestnut colour, well groomed and shining. It had four distinct legs and left distinct footprints. These showed circular impressions with a diameter (measured) of nine inches [22.8 cm] and the marks of claws about seven inches [17.8 cm] long extending outwards from the body. The creature travelled very fast. A kangaroo dog followed it to the water. When disturbed it reared up and turned on its hind legs. Its height, standing on the four legs, would be from 3ft 6in to 4ft [1.07 to 1.22 metres]."

The men were familiar with the seals and sea-leopards of that coast but this monster was not one of them.

4. There is more sea than land – it covers three-fifths of the Earth's surface. In places it is 6 miles (9.5 km) deep, and only a minute fraction has been explored. Enough room to give a home to many creatures that humans have never encountered.

5. The largest whales are 30 metres long, the largest known fish (the whale shark) up to 18 metres long.

6. Just when we think we know all the life forms in the oceans a new one is discovered – in 1937 a previously unknown beaked whale was washed ashore in New Zealand . . .

7. . . . and, just when we think all the prehistoric sea-creatures are extinct, a live one turns up. A coelacanth (believed to have died out 70 million years ago) was caught in the Indian Ocean in 1939. More have been caught since – alive and flapping.

8. Most of the Earth's ocean is in the southern half of the globe – but almost all of the fishing takes place in the north. The southern seas are almost undisturbed.

9. Stories of sea-monsters have been told by groups of people all over the world. The people are separated by thousands of miles and thousands of years . . . yet the monsters are often similar. In northern Europe it was called the Kraken. When it surfaced it spread itself out over a distance of a mile and a half [2.4 km]. Sailors who

mistook it for an island would land on it, light their camp-fires then be left to swim for it when the monster dived. In Malagasy legend it is called The Lord of the Sea; the Ancient Greeks told of the monstrous Scylla.

10. Dolphins swimming in line look like a many-humped creature, as do swimming penguins. Other known creatures that have been mistaken for sea-monsters include seals, walruses, sea-lions, enormous conger eels, sea-cows (now believed extinct), whales, octopuses, and giant squid which can reach 20 metres and have been seen to fight whales!

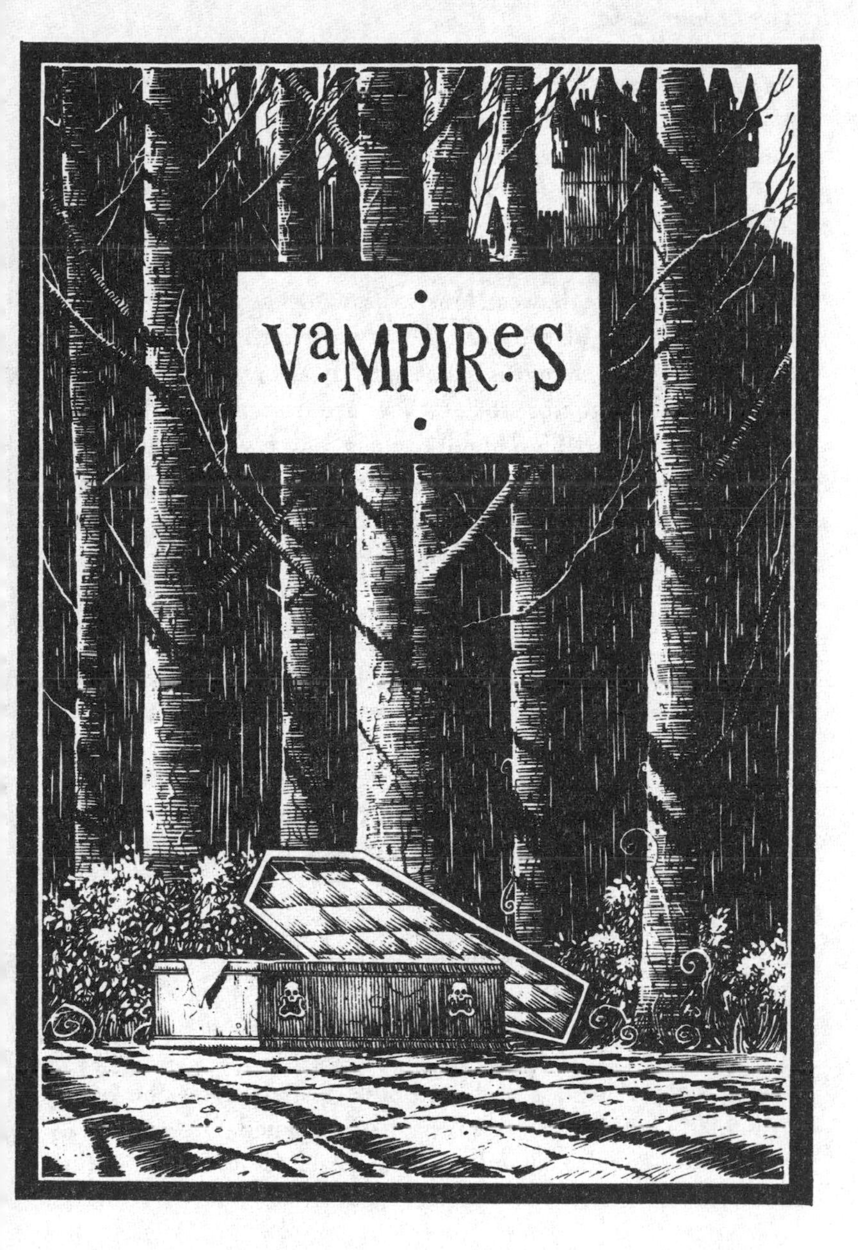
VAMPIRES

"Vampires issue forth from their graves in the night, attack people sleeping quietly in their beds, suck out all the blood from their bodies and destroy them."

John Heinrich Zopft, 1733

Vampires are the monsters of a nightmare. They are hard to recognize because they can look so human. They are hard to kill because they are already dead. They are hard to escape from because they can change into bats and fly after you. Yet, mixed in with the silly horror stories, there are true stories which are harder to explain. Two hundred years ago a very respectable group of lawyers, government officers and army officers reported on a series of strange goings-on in the Slavic regions and Baltic states of eastern Europe . . .

The Soldier's Story

The soldier stood to attention. He trembled as Colonel Linz shouted at him. "What are these stupid stories you have been spreading through the regiment, Private Koros?"

The soldier licked his lips. "Just the truth, sir!"

The commander sneered. "Truth? Truth! The truth is there are no such things as vampires."

"Yes, sir."

"What?"

"I mean no, sir. No such thing."

Colonel Linz strode up to the soldier and hissed, "You are a soldier in the Hungarian army – not some ignorant peasant."

"Yes, sir . . . I mean no, sir."

The colonel sighed and returned to his seat at the desk. "Stand at ease, Koros. Tell me what happened."

The soldier relaxed and ran a finger round his collar. "I'm not living in the army camp, sir. I've been sent out to live in the village – or rather, a farm on the edge of the village. A family called Bruck. They're nice, friendly people; treat me as one of the family."

The colonel just grunted.

"Then one night we were sitting down for dinner. We'd just started eating when the door swung open and this terrible smell drifted into the room. Made me feel quite sick. That's when the old man walked in. An ordinary bloke. Clothes a bit old fashioned, eyes a bit red. The smell seemed to be coming from *him*. There was nothing particularly strange about him. Like I said, he was just an old man. I thought it must have been a neighbour. But the family just froze like they'd seen a ghost."

"Yes," the colonel nodded. "Go on!"

"He didn't say a word. He just walked round the table till he came to the farmer, Mr Bruck, and sort of rested a hand on his shoulder. Then he walked out."

"What did the family do?" the colonel demanded.

Private Koros shrugged. "The daughters ran out of the room crying. Mrs Bruck just sat in her chair looking like she'd seen the devil himself. All she said was, "He'll be dead before sunrise.""

"And farmer Bruck? What did he do?"

The soldier shuddered. "He stood up, walked to his room and lay on the bed. Never got up again. The next day he was dead. Like Mrs Bruck said he'd be."

The colonel ran a hand over his iron-grey hair. "What exactly *did* Mrs Bruck say?"

"She *said* the old man was Mr Bruck's father . . . and he'd died ten years ago!"

Colonel Linz brought his fist crashing down. "Imagination! You never saw the old man."

"Yes, sir . . . I mean no, sir."

"What did your captain do when you told him the story?"

"Went to the graveyard and had the old man's body dug up, sir."

"Hah! There wouldn't be much more than a skeleton left after ten years," the colonel snorted.

Koros shook his head slowly. "The body was as fresh as if he'd died yesterday," he murmured.

"Imagination!" the commander barked. "And where did these stories about blood-drinking vampires come from? That's what I've been sent here to investigate. More fairy tales and lies, I suppose?"

"If you say so, sir," Koros said miserably. "But the villagers did tell us about another vampire in the region. He came back and killed three of his nieces in a fortnight. He was attacking his fourth niece when he was interrupted. The girl is dying. The villagers think the vampire escaped back to his grave."

Colonel Linz stood up. "Good! Then we can examine this grave right now. We shall put an end to these stories once and for all."

The soldier smiled. "Yes, sir."

"And to put your mind at rest, Koros, you can come and watch!"

The smile slid from the private's face. "Yes, sir," he said weakly.

And, to make it worse, he was given a spade and told to dig. Curious soldiers and frightened villagers gathered around as Koros started to unearth the coffin. The afternoon shadows had lengthened into evening by the time he had finished. At last the coffin was lifted clear and Colonel Linz stepped forward to take the spade from Koros. "Now!" he announced. "Let's have a look at this so-called vampire."

He swung the spade over his head and smashed the wooden

coffin lid into splinters. He stepped back as the foul smell hit him. The crowd gasped and shrank away at the sight that greeted them. The body was in perfect condition. Koros swore that he could see the heart still beating!

He snatched the spade from Colonel Linz and drove it deep into the heart of the vampire. A foul white liquid oozed out. Some of the onlookers thought they heard a hideous scream . . . but in the confusion it was hard to tell. One thing was certain. The heart was no longer beating.

The body was destroyed with quick-lime and peace returned to the village. Strangely, from that moment, the fourth niece began at last to recover from her attack.

Colonel Linz and the official enquiry returned to Belgrade to make their report. And Private Koros lived to be an older and wiser man. "Vampires?" he used to say when the subject came up in the taverns around the flickering log fires. "Vampires?" he shuddered. "I once knew a man who said there's no such thing . . ."

Vampire legends come from all over the world. They concern the 'undead' – the dead who rise again. Russian vampires are believed to have purple faces and are the human form of someone who, when alive, opposed the church.

In other countries vampires are easier to spot because of their curious features or disgusting habits. Bulgarian vampires have only one nostril; Bavarian vampires sleep with one eye open and thumbs linked; Brazilian vampires have their feet covered in a velvety fur while Albanian vampires can be seen wearing high heels. Chinese vampires draw their strength from the moon. Mexican vampires have no flesh on their skulls.

But most fearsome seem to be the vampires from the Rocky Mountains – they use their noses to suck their victims' blood out through the ears.

It would be wrong to think that vampire legends only exist in the distant past in some hidden corner of Europe. They persist in modern cities . . .

The Policeman's Story

I've been in the police force a long time now. In all those years I've seen some strange things – met some strange people. But the strangest thing – and the strangest person – was the case of the man who was killed by a vampire.

It's true . . . in a way. It happened back in January 1973. I was a young detective constable at the time, on duty in Stoke-on-Trent – that's in the English Midlands, as you may know.

Sounded like a routine case. I was sent to number Three, The Villas. The neighbours had reported that a seventy-year-old man had not been seen for a few days. Nothing strange about that. People often go missing. Usually we find them alive.

Mrs Ledger at number Two was a worried woman. "You reported your neighbour missing?" I said as she answered the door.

She nodded. I took out my notebook. "Mr Myiciura," she said.

"Er, could you spell that?" I asked.

"No. Can't you?" she replied.

I sighed. I made a guess at the spelling. "Funny name."

"Polish," she explained.

"And what makes you think he's missing?"

She shrugged herself into a worn old cardigan. "Milk bottles on the doorstep. I always see him to say hello to in the morning, and I haven't seen him for three days."

"That's Wednesday?" I noted. "Have you knocked at his door?"

"This afternoon," she said carefully. Her small eyes glittered in the light from the street lamp. "He doesn't like people knocking," she said in a hoarse whisper. "He's scared."

"Scared? Scared of what?"

Mrs Ledger leaned forward and her eyes flickered up and down the dark street. "Scared of things that come for you in the night."

I began to put my notebook away. It was clear I was dealing with a crank here. She shot out an arm and with a rough hand stopped me. "No! Honest. He came here after the last war with nothing. He ran away from the Germans. They killed his wife and family. Scared him witless it did!"

"And he thinks the Germans are still after him?" I asked.

She shook her thin head. "No. But he's a nervous man. He's had a hard life, and I wouldn't like to see anything happen to him. Poor old bloke. Poor, lonely old man," she sighed. Mrs Ledger looked as if she knew what it was to be poor and lonely. "Don't frighten him, eh?"

"I'll try," I promised, and walked the few steps to number Three.

I let the heavy iron knocker fall against the door. The knock boomed through the house like a tomb. An empty house with bare walls and floors. I'd seen a lot of houses like that in my time.

I waited as Mrs Ledger shivered in the shadow of her doorway. I tried the door. It was locked. I pushed it with my shoulder and the rotten old wood gave way. Another push and it splintered inwards. I found myself in a dark hallway that smelled of cabbage and old socks. I groped for a light switch, found a cold metal one and clicked it down. Nothing happened.

Mrs Ledger's voice came from the doorway. "He won't have electric in the house," she explained. "Too scared."

Luckily I carried a torch. I stepped towards the door on the right of the hall. My feet crunched in something powdery. The torch showed white crystals. Strung around the door were withered white bulbs.

The door to the room opened with a creak when I pushed it. My torch caught the pale, frightened face of the old man on the bed. He didn't move. Those wild, wide eyes didn't blink in the beam of the torch. I knew he was dead.

I closed the door softly and went off to call for assistance.

The first tests showed that he had choked to death. Choked on a pickled onion. There had to be an inquiry into the death – an inquest led by a coroner.

"A sad case," the coroner declared. "But people have been known to choke to death on their food before now." He turned to me. "Anything to add, constable?"

I swallowed hard. I could have let the case rest there. But I had decided to take a trip to the local public library before the inquest. Eventually I had come across a book called *The Natural History of the Vampire* that seemed to have the answer; that's how I knew what had scared old Myiciura to death.

I turned to the coroner. "Er, yes, sir," I said.

The coroner looked over the top of his glasses at me. "Well?"

I took a deep breath. "There were white crystals scattered all over his floor and over his bed. The lab report confirms that this was in fact salt. A packet of salt was found at the feet of the deceased."

The coroner looked a little blank but said, "Go on."

"The bulbs around the door proved to be garlic," I said.

"And what do you deduce from that, constable?" he asked.

"That Mr Myiciura was terribly afraid of vampires," I said.

The coroner blinked and the glasses almost fell off his nose. "Are you suggesting that he died as the result of a vampire attack? There were no marks on the body!"

"No, sir," I said quickly. "Just that he may have died of the *fear* of a vampire attack. In eastern Europe I believe people are convinced that such creatures exist."

The coroner sat back, took off his glasses and rubbed his eyes. "Very well. We will postpone this case for two weeks for further tests."

He left a stunned courtroom with some reporters, who were scribbling furiously about this ordinary case that had turned out to be a sensation.

But I was in the office when the new test results came in. Mr Myiciura *had* died of choking – but not on a pickled onion. He had choked on one of his own cloves of garlic.

The terrified man had slept with one in his mouth to keep away the vampires. As he fell asleep the garlic slid into his throat and choked him.

In a curious way, the vampires got him after all.

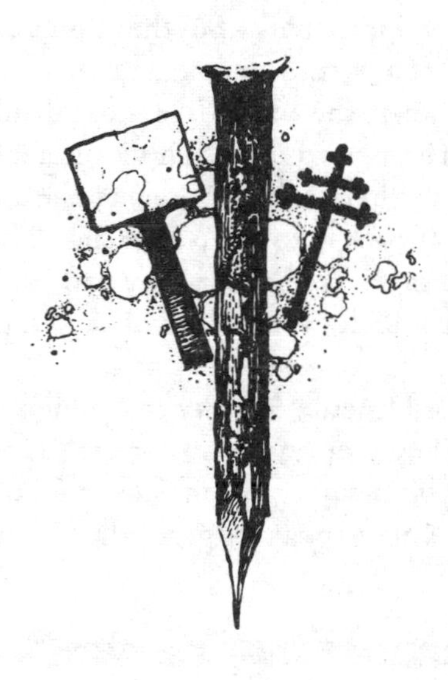

Vampires – FACT FILE

1. The famous vampire Count Dracula is just a story written by Bram Stoker 100 years ago. That story is still popular today. Another story-book monster is almost forgotten today. He appeared in 1847, 50 years before Bram Stoker's *Dracula*. He was called *Varney the Vampire* and appeared in a serial story of 220 episodes. Varney died when he threw himself into a volcano.

2. There *was* a man called Dracula who lived in eastern Europe – but he wasn't a vampire. Just a very cruel war-lord who terrorized the region. He was known as Vlad Dracula The Impaler through his vicious treatment of enemies and prisoners whom he impaled on sharp, pointed wooden stakes.

3. There *are* vampire bats – but they don't usually suck human blood. They find sleeping cattle or horses, nip the skin and lap at the blood like a cat drinking milk. Their teeth are so sharp that their victim feels nothing. A substance in their saliva prevents the blood from clotting and allows it to keep flowing. Their blood-drinking will rarely kill – but they can carry diseases such as rabies which eventually kill the victim.

4. There is a Dracula Society in London and one in California. They meet once a year on 8 November to celebrate the birthday of Bram Stoker who wrote the book *Dracula*. Guest speakers give talks on the vampire legends.

5. Traditionally people believe that garlic and salt will keep vampires away and even poison them. Sprinkling chalk and holy water is also supposed to be effective. But the only sure way to kill a vampire is to force a wooden or iron stake through its heart. Vampires have been reported to scream when this is done. Some are even supposed to cry. Those who want to be certain the vampire is dead will cut off the head and have the body burned.

6. Traditionally people believe that they can protect themselves from vampires by making the sign of the cross. Vampires don't like the Church, and the Church doesn't like vampires. The churches of eastern Europe used to claim that anyone leading a wicked life could become a vampire. They also believed that a victim could not be forced to enter the vampire's lair. An invitation had to be offered by free choice if the vampire was to succeed.

7. Vampire legends go back many thousands of years to Greek, Roman and Hebrew mythology. But the strongest legends centre around Transylvania in Romania, eastern Europe. The Romanians have a popular tourist industry based on the stories; they have opened a *Castle Dracula* hotel with tape-recorded wolves howling as visitors drive towards it.

8. Legends say that a vampire can be a man or a woman. The victim of a vampire is said to become a vampire in turn. Eating the earth from the vampire's grave can be a cure, however.

9. In the 17th and 18th centuries body-snatchers stole corpses from graves and sold them to doctors for medical experiments. The body-snatchers left the graves empty. Ignorant and frightened people thought that the corpses had found their own way out.

10. Those who believe in vampires explain their undead state in two ways: vampires are evil spirits that take over corpses and use them; vampires are the spirits of dead people who were too wicked to be allowed into the after-life – they have to return to their old body to find a 'home'.

WEREWOLVES

Even he who is pure of heart
And says his prayers by night
May become a wolf when the wolfbane blooms
And the moon is full and bright.

Traditional European proverb

Werewolf stories are among the oldest horror stories in the world. They probably began with legends of Norse gods who had powers to change themselves into animals – including wolves. The stories were given extra power by country people who lived in fear of real wolves; then there were actual cases of mentally ill people who believed they were animals and tried to eat raw flesh to prove it.

A disease of the body called Hypertrichosis can cause the body and entire face to be covered in hair. This too could have led ignorant people to believe that the sufferer was infected by a werewolf.

No matter how impossible it seems for a human to change shape some people will always believe in werewolves. People like the Reverend Montague Summers, a well-known 19th century writer on the supernatural. He described an encounter which he said happened in Wales in 1888 . . .

Professor Richard Eldon was pleased with himself. He stood at the door of the mountain cottage and breathed the clear Merionethshire air. "Wonderful, Avril!" he cried to his wife. "Didn't I tell you I'd give you the best holiday you've ever had?"

Avril Eldon had spent an hour unpacking their cases. She had lit the fire in the stove and begun to cook an evening meal.

Her husband had spent that hour on the porch of the cottage smoking his pipe and staring at the mountains shimmering in the sun. "Wonderful views . . . and so peaceful. Nothing can disturb us here. We can really relax."

The woman staggered into the cottage with an armful of logs and said pointedly, "Can you, dear?"

Her husband didn't seem to notice the edge in her voice. "Ye-es. We can walk up those mountains tomorrow," he promised.

Avril pushed a wisp of hair from her brow and winced. "Oh, good," she said flatly. "First you could help me make the beds. The linen's in the cupboard and it needs taking out now. It'll have to be aired before we sleep in it tonight."

The professor pulled a large watch out of his waistcoat pocket. "Hmm. If I'm going to get any fishing in today I'll have to set off now," he sighed and turned to pick up his fishing basket. "You'll manage."

His wife opened her mouth to object but he went on, "That seems fair enough to me. You make the beds while I catch our supper . . . I'll be back before sunset," he promised as he marched down the hillside.

The professor returned at sunset, just as he'd promised, but without the fish he'd said he'd bring.

"Sorry, my love," he sighed. "There don't seem to be any fish in that lake – or, if there are, then something's scaring them away."

"Just as well I made a shepherd's pie, then," his wife sniffed.

He dropped his fishing basket on the white table-cloth and Avril reached forward quickly to lift it off. "That's clean!" she cried. Then, feeling the weight of the basket, she added, "Well, you must have caught something."

The professor blinked. "What? Oh, yes. Almost forgot. I found a fascinating thing down by the lake . . . most unusual."

He opened the wicker basket and took out a huge skull. Avril wasn't usually upset at the sight of bones. But something about this skull disgusted her. "What on earth is it?"

Her husband shrugged. "Thought we'd take it back to the college at the end of the holiday. One of the chaps in the science department might tell us. It's not a sheep – too big."

"And those huge teeth belong to a meat-eater," his wife added. "Some sort of dog?"

"I've never seen a dog that big. That's why it's so exciting. I thought it could be prehistoric," the man said proudly. "Just pop it on that shelf for now. We'll look at it again after supper."

But after supper the professor had other plans. "The pub?" his wife groaned. "You're going to the pub down in the village and leaving me here alone?"

The man shrugged. "Tore my trousers on some bushes down by the lake. Thought you could darn them for me. It'll keep you occupied. See you later. Shouldn't be more than a couple of hours," he promised as he vanished through the door.

Avril Eldon lit one of the oil-lamps in the cottage and took out her sewing basket. As she bent over her mending she noticed that the room was growing brighter. Looking up she saw the moon rising over the mountains and flooding through the window. The mountains were black and deserted and silent.

A soft snuffling sound was the first hint that she was not alone. She looked up sharply. The empty eyes of the skull stared down at her from the shelf. Then there was a sharp scraping at the door as if some dog was asking to come in.

Avril put down her needle and walked over to check that the door was fastened tight. There was a small window beside the door. As she reached it a shadow blotted out the moonlight. The huge face of an enormous dog was peering in at her with great, glowing eyes.

The eyes were fixed on her, willing her to open the door. But she knew she had to fight them and forced her own eyes shut, blindly finding the beam that barred the door.

She leaned with her back to the door and saw those eyes in her mind. Intelligent eyes . . . human eyes. And weren't those paws on the sill more like human hands?

Suddenly she remembered the front door. Racing through the house she reached the bolts just as the latch rattled. She heard the creature panting hungrily. It snarled when the door refused to give and growled as it walked around the house looking for another way in.

The woman sank, trembling, to the floor and pressed her back to the door, her legs too weak to move. Time and again the beast barged and bumped against the door. Then Avril did something she hadn't done for years. She prayed. She said every prayer she could remember from her days in Sunday School and a few that she made up on the spot. When she stopped mumbling the Lord's Prayer for the last time she was surprised to find that the noises had gone.

She rose weakly to her feet and laughed at her own nervous state. "Just a dog," she muttered. "Just a dog."

Then she froze as the gravel outside the door rattled and the latch clattered.

Thump! Thump! Thump! The door shook.

Then a voice. A human voice. A voice she hardly recognized. "Avril! Open the door, woman! Avril!"

Her trembling hands pulled back the bolts and tugged the door open. She dragged her husband inside and quickly locked them in again.

The professor blinked. "What's wrong, my dear? You look as if you've seen a ghost!"

Avril shook her head slowly. "No. Something much, much

worse than any ghost." And she told her husband about the ghastly visitor.

Professor Eldon frowned. "That ties up with something the villagers told me in the pub. Some story about that lake being haunted by a man-wolf. What was it they called it? Yes. A werewolf. Just as well I came prepared for some shooting," he said grimly as he slid a rifle out of its leather case. He checked that it was loaded and sat at the table staring out into the night.

Hours passed. The couple kept up their unblinking watch. Then as the moon sank, and even the owls had returned to their nests, the face of the wolf with the eyes of a man appeared at the window. Professor Eldon snatched his gun and ran to the door. The wolf saw the movement and fled ahead of him.

Even in the darkness of that mountain night the creature had its own greenish, ghoulish glow. The man followed the beast down the path to the lake.

The werewolf stopped at the edge of the lake, turned and looked back with its hot-coal eyes. As the professor raised the rifle to fire, the creature howled and plunged itself into the lake.

But as it hit the water it disappeared without a splash, without a ripple.

The man staggered with exhaustion towards the cottage. His wife was standing behind him. In her hands she held the ivory skull.

Without a word he nodded, took it from her hands and walked to the edge of the water. He threw it as far into the lake as he could. Putting his arm around his wife's shoulder he walked back to the cottage.

The sunrise came.

The werewolf was never seen again.

Peace returned to the lake. But peace never returned to the Eldons. The monster lived on in their minds and troubled their dreams for ever after.

Monster Werewolf – FACT FILE

1. A werewolf is said to be rather like a vampire when they are both in human form. They have small, pointed ears, hair on the palms of their clawed hands and eyebrows that meet in the middle. The werewolf, however, has the ring finger of each hand a little longer than the middle finger – in humans and vampires the middle finger is longer.

2. Superstitious people believe that if you sleep outdoors when a full moon falls on a Friday, then you may turn into a werewolf. Eating the plant wolfbane can have this effect too.

3. Human shape-changers can take many forms depending on where in the world they are: in Africa people believed in wereleopards, in India weretigers, in Scandinavia, werebears.

4. Wereanimal stories are often linked with stories of witchcraft. The theory was that witches could turn themselves into animals whenever they wanted. The animal was often a hare, because it could sprint away from witch-hunters, but was often a cat or a toad. In the 1500s the wolf was added to the list of witch forms.

5. If attacked by a werewolf then, Canadians say, a good defence is to speak the name of Christ. The French recommend taking three drops of the wolf's blood. The

most famous method, favoured by film-makers, is to take the silver from a church crucifix, mould it into the shape of a bullet and shoot the werewolf.

6. Werewolves are believed to grow hair *inside* their bodies. Sadly one suspect died in Italy in 1541 when his accusers tried to prove this by cutting him open. He was innocent of course – but that was no comfort to the dead man's family.

7. A *Lycanthrope* is a mentally-ill person who believes he has taken the form of a wolf. In 1589 Peter Stump of Cologne, Germany, confessed to changing himself magically into a wolf. That is unlikely, but what is certain is that he killed many human and animal victims while overcome by the illness.

8. A twelfth-century poem tells of a knight who was a werewolf three days of the week but had no savage habits. His unfaithful wife had a lover; the lover stole the knight's clothes while he was in werewolf shape. Without his clothes the werewolf could not regain his human form and return to being a knight.

9. If a werewolf is wounded in its wolf form then its human form will suffer a similar wound. For example, cut off the wolf's paw and it becomes a man with a missing hand. This is known as *wound-doubling*.

10. King John of England was not only unpopular, he was also supposed to be a werewolf. After his death his body could not rest in holy ground; a Norman manuscript says that some monks heard him moving underground so they dug him up and reburied him outside holy ground.

TRUE HORROR STORIES

For Debbie with thanks

INTRODUCTION

Newcastle, England – April 1992

The building I worked in used to be a huge private house. The downstairs rooms were large and grand with tall windows – but the higher you climbed the smaller and darker the corridors and rooms became.

My office was on the top floor. This must have been where the servants lived in the old days of the splendid hall.

One Thursday morning, at eleven o'clock, I reached the top landing and pulled open the door that led into a dimly-lit corridor. As I began to walk through the doorway a figure rushed towards me. It was a woman. She was small – the top of her head would have barely reached my chin. She had white hair, a long grey dress and a white apron.

I could see in that moment that her white-haired head was bent forward – she wasn't looking where she was going. There was no time or space for me to get out of her way. I flinched, closed my eyes and turned my head. I waited for the collision.

It never came. I opened my eyes. I blinked. There was no one there. I laughed at my own stupidity and forgot about the grey-haired, grey-dressed woman.

I returned to the building about seven-thirty that night. There was a late meeting in the great hall downstairs. My notes were in my office at the top of the stairs.

"Is the office open?" I asked the caretaker.

An old cleaner who'd worked in the building for over twenty years overheard me.

"You're not going upstairs at this time of night, are you?" she asked.

"Why not?" I shrugged.

"You wouldn't catch me going up there after dark . . . not for a million pounds."

"I'm not scared of the dark," I told her.

She shook her head. "Be careful . . . you might meet the Grey Lady!"

"Grey Lady?" I asked and felt a cold slug of fear run down my back. Somehow I knew what the cleaner was going to say.

"Yes! Didn't you know? The top floor's haunted by an old servant."

It was growing dark outside – and darker inside by now. This time my hand was trembling, just a little, as I reached the door at the top of the stairs. And I saw . . . nothing.

But what had I seen that morning? Perhaps I imagined I'd seen a woman in grey . . . but I'd never heard about the grey lady when I met her. Perhaps I'm a liar . . . only I can be certain that I'm not. Or perhaps I saw a ghost . . . a real horror from another world.

What is certain is that I wanted to know more about the supernatural. That's when the strangest thing of all happened. The day after I'd seen (or imagined) the Grey Lady, I received a letter. It asked me if I'd write a collection of true horror stories.

Here it is. A collection of ghosts and ghouls and murders and mysteries to make you wonder and to make you think.

Everyone loves a good chilling tale. But are there really such horrifying things in this world? Look at some of the stories here – stories that some people at some time have sworn are true. Then look at some of the facts that surround those stories and try to make up your mind.

Truth or lies? Fake or mistake?

But take care not to read them after dark! YOU HAVE BEEN WARNED!

LIZZIE BORDEN'S
·A·X·E

Some murders are so horrible that they are remembered long, long after.

Fall River, USA – 1892

The Bordens were the most important family in the town of Fall River. They had been there for hundreds of years. Yet the Bordens' house was not so very grand. Old Andrew Borden was too careful with his money for that. A cold, hard, loveless man, in 1892 he was seventy years old. He would not live to see seventy-one.

Number 92 Second Street was comfortable enough for Andrew Borden and his family. Comfortable but not grand. The house was warm in winter. Down in the basement was a coal-fired furnace. Near the furnace was a chopping block with a stack of wood for lighting the fire. And near the chopping block was an axe for splitting the wood into sticks.

There were four women in the house: Andrew's daughters Emma and Lizzie, their step-mother, Abby Borden, and the maidservant, Bridget. Mrs Abby Borden was sixty-three years old in 1892. She would not live to see sixty-four.

Abby never managed to take the place of Emma and Lizzie's mother in the hearts of the two young women. Number 92 Second Street was not a happy house.

Lizzie was thirty-two in 1892. She had learned meanness from her father. So she was disgusted and angry when her father gave a gift of land to his wife's family. She never forgave and she never forgot – something seemed to snap in Lizzie's strange mind.

"Lizzie!" Mrs Abby Borden said one day. "I haven't seen my cat for ages. Do you know where he is?"

Lizzie wasn't beautiful, but her large, light eyes were the most attractive thing about her. "Go downstairs and you'll find your cat," she promised, and those eyes glowed with pleasure.

Mrs Borden went down to the cellar and found the cat . . . it had been laid across the chopping block and someone had cut off its head with the wood axe.

But that was nothing to what happened on the morning of 4 August 1892. A hot and humid morning. Even at a quarter past six in the morning, the sun was blazing hot as maidservant Bridget struggled downstairs to light the cooking stove. She felt ill. Everyone in the house had been ill the day before – maybe from eating meat that had gone bad in the summer heat. Emma was spared because she was away on holiday.

After breakfast Mrs Borden went upstairs to lie down. She was still unwell from the food-poisoning of the day before. Mr Borden went into town to do business while Bridget set about cleaning the windows.

By twenty to eleven Mr Borden had returned. He struggled with the locks on the front door. Someone had pushed the bolt in so hard that Bridget could hardly open it to let her master in.

Lizzie stood at the top of the stairs. She laughed.

Mr Borden strode in. "Where's your mother?"

"Out. She had a message to go and visit someone who's sick," Lizzie answered.

"Who?"

"I don't know, Father."

"They can't be sick as me," the old man snapped. "I still feel weak from yesterday. I think I'll lie down in the sitting room."

Lizzie smiled. It was two minutes to eleven. Bridget went back to washing windows as Lizzie set up an ironing board and started ironing handkerchiefs.

"Excuse me, Miss Lizzie, but I feel sick again," the girl groaned. "If you don't mind I'll just lie down." The maidservant climbed up to her attic bedroom. The City Hall clock was striking eleven.

Bridget lay down on her bed. Ten minutes later she heard

Lizzie cry out, "Bridget! Oh, Bridget! Come down!"

Bridget struggled from her bed. "What's wrong, Miss Lizzie?"

"Come down quickly! Father's dead! Somebody's come in and killed him!" Lizzie shouted.

Bridget went to the sitting room to look. Lizzie stopped her. "No! Don't go in there. Go and get a doctor! Run!"

But Bridget couldn't find the local doctor. She left a message with the doctor's wife and hurried back to number 92 Second Street.

"How did it happen?" the girl groaned. "Where were you, Miss Lizzie?"

"In the garden," Lizzie Borden sighed. "When I came back in the door was open wide."

A neighbour, Mrs Churchill, saw the frantic women and came across to find out what was wrong. She opened the door to the sitting room. Andrew Borden lay on the settee where he'd gone to rest. His feet were on the floor. His head was resting on the arm. But it was a head that no one would have recognised.

There were eleven cuts between his nose and ear; one blow had sliced his eye in half and another had almost cut his nose clean off. Blood spattered the floor, the wall, the sofa – but Andrew Borden hadn't moved. His murderer had slaughtered him as he slept.

Mrs Churchill backed out of the room. "Where were you when it happened?" she gasped.

"In the barn," Lizzie murmured.

"Your poor mother must be told. Where is she?"

Lizzie shrugged, helpless. "She went to visit a sick friend. I don't know who."

Mrs Churchill took charge. She sent messages for the doctor and the police. By half past eleven she had returned to the house of death on Second Street.

"If only we could find your mother, Lizzie. Maybe we should send a message to her friend, Mrs Whitehead!"

"No!" Lizzie answered sharply. "I'm sure I heard her come in the front and go up to her room! Bridget, go and see."

But shaking, sickly Bridget wouldn't go alone.

"I'll go with you," Mrs Churchill offered. The two set off up the front stairs. They didn't need to climb quite to the top. The bedroom door was open. Bridget stopped. Behind the bed, half hidden, lay Abby Borden's body.

Mrs Churchill pushed past the rigid maidservant and looked at the gruesome sight. Nineteen blows had rained down on the back of her head and one had chopped deep into her neck. But the blood had dried and started to turn dark. It seemed that Abby Borden had died some time before her husband.

No note was ever found. The truth was that Abby Borden had never left the house. She must have died soon after breakfast.

And Lizzie had never gone into the barn. The floor was dry and thick with dust. The first policeman in the barn would swear that there was not a single footprint in the dust. Could Lizzie have lied?

Lizzie was the one the police suspected. But Lizzie was a Borden. A lady from the finest family in Fall River. Surely she could not have butchered both her stepmother and her father . . . could she?

In that hot house which was home to such cold, cold people, Lizzie Borden stayed cooler than ice. As her parents' corpses still lay in their blood-stained rooms she said calmly, "I think I'd prefer them to be buried by undertaker Winwood."

The next night, Lizzie placed an advert in the local paper:

$5,000 Dollar reward

The above reward will be paid to anyone who may secure
THE ARREST AND CONVICTION
of the person or persons who are responsible for the deaths of
MR ANDREW I BORDEN AND HIS WIFE

That same Friday the Fall River police found a new, amazing fact. The day before the murders Lizzie Borden had been to a local chemist's shop and tried to buy some prussic acid . . . perhaps the deadliest poison known!

On Saturday the funeral was held for Abby and Andrew Borden.

On Sunday Lizzie was seen trying to burn an old dress. "Why are you doing that?" a friend asked.

"It's covered with paint," she said.

"But it looks so suspicious, trying to burn old clothes! The police will say you're trying to hide blood stains!"

"Ah!" Lizzie gasped. "I didn't think. I only wish you'd stopped me!" But mean Lizzie Borden had burned a dress that was only ten weeks old . . . something unheard of in the penny-pinching Borden house.

And one week after the murders the Fall River police arrested Lizzie Borden for the crime. The trial was almost a year later and in the middle of another heat wave. It was ninety-three degrees Fahrenheit outside the courtroom and hotter still inside.

On a table lay a bag. It was covered with tissue paper. The lawyer threw a piece of evidence onto the table – one of Lizzie's dresses. The dress caught the bag and the tissue flew off. Now Lizzie could see what was in the bag – the shattered skulls of her father and stepmother! Lizzie fell into a dead faint at the shock. But the shock was not great enough to make her confess.

She sat silent through the days of the trial. At last her lawyer pleaded that the jury must either set poor Lizzie free, or be blamed for placing a hangman's noose around her neck. He reminded them that Andrew Borden had gone to his grave wearing a ring that was a gift from Lizzie. "To find her guilty," he finished, "you must find her a fiend! Does she look it?"

The twelve men of the jury looked at Andrew Borden's little

girl. Her large, pale eyes looked back. Eyes that had never shed a tear for the deaths. Yet, as her lawyer claimed,

"The eyes that cannot weep
Are the saddest eyes of all."

The judge turned to her and asked, "Lizzie Borden, have you any words you wish to say to this jury?"

She rose slowly to her feet, bowed to the judge and looked straight at the twelve men. "I am innocent. I leave it to my counsel to speak for me." Thirteen words. The only words that Lizzie Borden spoke at her own trial.

The jury voted. The clerk of the court asked, "Gentlemen of the jury, have you reached your verdict?"

"We have."

"What do you say?"

"Not guilty!"

A huge cheer swept the courtroom. Lizzie sat back in her seat and at last managed a tear – in sheer relief that her neck had been saved. "Take me home," she muttered. "Take me home. I want to go to the old place tonight."

And Lizzie went back to the house of death and lived with the ghosts of her butchered father and stepmother. She died thirty-four years after the trial, in 1927. Her sister, Emma, died nine days later.

Lizzie Borden left over a million dollars in her will. Some say that Lizzie got away with murder.

So who killed the Bordens?

There are three explanations. Read them all then decide which you think is the most likely.

The Hidden Killer – FACT FILE

1. Mr Andrew Borden was not a popular man. There must have been many men and women in Fall River who wanted to see him dead.

2. The killer slipped poison into the Bordens' milk on Wednesday morning, 3 August, 1892. It made them all sick but didn't kill them. So, on the morning of 4 August, the killer crept into the Borden house while Mrs Borden and Lizzie were upstairs. The maid, Bridget, rushed out to be sick and left the back door open. The killer waited.

3. Mrs Borden received a note asking her to visit a sick friend. Mr Borden returned home feeling ill and lay down to sleep. The killer crept out and, with one of the axes from the Borden cellar, hacked Andrew Borden to death. The killer was forced to hide because Lizzie came back from the barn and started ironing in the next room.

4. Lizzie discovered the body and Mrs Churchill sent for the police. While Mrs Churchill went for help, Mrs Abby Borden came home. The killer followed her upstairs and murdered her with the same axe. The killer escaped out of the front door while the police were coming to the back door.

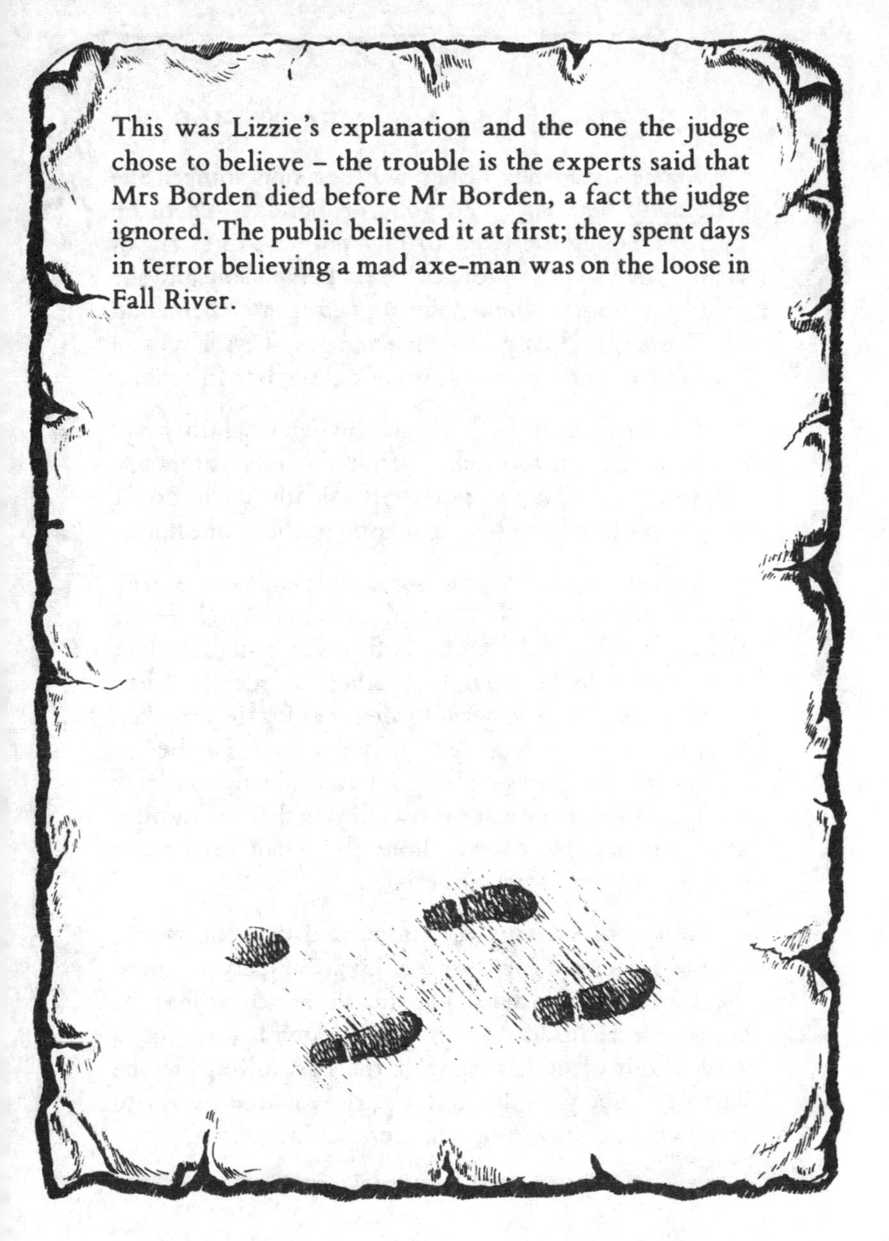

This was Lizzie's explanation and the one the judge chose to believe – the trouble is the experts said that Mrs Borden died before Mr Borden, a fact the judge ignored. The public believed it at first; they spent days in terror believing a mad axe-man was on the loose in Fall River.

The Deadly Daughter – FACT FILE

1. Lizzie hated her father and her stepmother. She waited till her sister had gone on holiday. Then, on Tuesday 2 August, tried to buy poison to get rid of them. The chemist wouldn't sell her poison but she found some somewhere. She slipped it into their food on Wednesday 3 August – she even gave herself a little so no one would suspect. It wasn't enough to kill them.

2. On the morning of 4 August, when her father had left the house, she took an axe from the cellar, crept upstairs and hacked her stepmother to death. She had over an hour to clean herself up before her father came home.

3. When her father came home and lay down to sleep she killed him too. She still had ten minutes to hide the axe and wash off the blood before she called Bridget down and told her that her father was dead. When Bridget asked where Mrs Borden was Lizzie panicked and came up with the stupid story that there had been a note calling her to a sick friend. Later, Lizzie was stuck with this story even after it was shown that her mother had been dead for over an hour and a half before this imaginary letter was delivered.

4. When Mrs Churchill announced that she would have to search for Mrs Borden, Lizzie quickly invented the story that she'd heard her stepmother come into the house. She realised that all of the blood had not been washed out of her dress after the first killing, so she burned it. She gambled that a jury would not want to see a woman hang. She won her gamble.

This is the story believed by most people.

The Murderous Maid – FACT FILE

1. Bridget had had enough of the Bordens. They were mean and thoughtless people to work for. She tried to poison them. She even took a little poison herself so that no one would suspect her. After all, Bridget did the cooking. She was the obvious person to put poison in the food.

2. It didn't work on the Bordens but Bridget woke up feeling ill. Then, to cap it all, on one of the hottest days in the history of Fall River, Mrs Borden ordered Bridget to clean all of the windows, inside and out.

3. Bridget sweated, carrying buckets of water from the barn and using a heavy brush to reach the upstairs windows. She went into the house to clean the inside windows and saw Mrs Borden kneeling on the floor over a large piece of embroidery. It was so easy!

4. Bridget tiptoed downstairs, took the axe from the cellar and crept back to Mrs Borden's room. The old woman was still kneeling over the tapestry. Bridget raised the axe and smashed it down into the skull of the old woman. In a frenzy she kept smashing down until she was exhausted.

5. She took the chance to clean her dress the next time she went to the barn for water. When Mr Borden returned she made an excuse to Lizzie and said that she needed a rest. As Lizzie went out to the barn Bridget killed the sleeping Mr Borden. He was killed with fewer, weaker blows – Bridget was too exhausted to do more.

6. Lizzie came in and found the body. Bridget told Lizzie that Lizzie would be blamed! She suggested that a story about Mrs Borden called out of the house would help! And no wonder Bridget refused to go up to Mrs Borden's bedroom alone . . . she knew what she'd find!

This was the story put forward by one writer who studied the case.

There is a murder committed in the USA about once every half an hour. But the horrific Borden killings are still remembered whenever people meet together and the subject turns to murder. American children have no doubt who was to blame. They have a playground rhyme that goes:

Lizzie Borden took an axe
And gave her mother forty whacks:
When she saw what she had done
She gave her father forty-one!

NIGHTMARE
F·A·R·M

Some ghosts seem to haunt the place they died and act out the way they died . . . to the horror of the living.

Brittany, France – August 1951

It never rains but it pours, John Allen thought. He trudged along the muddy French lane and cursed his luck.

He'd arrived in France that morning and stepped off the ferry to enjoy his cycling holiday. First came the rain to spoil it. Then cars rushing past him on the west roads had thrown up clouds of drenching spray.

So John had turned off the main road and onto the quiet country tracks, hoping for an easier journey. That was his first mistake. The rain had grown heavier, but now he was in the middle of the countryside with nowhere to shelter.

As he churned through muddy puddles, he didn't see the broken bottle lying at the bottom of one of them. He heard the splintering of the glass and the sudden bang as his tyre burst.

John sighed and climbed off his cycle to look at the damage. A ripped inner tube. He carried a puncture repair kit, but this was no small puncture – it was a large split. He tried to mend it. But the rain washed over the rubber and no patch would stick. It needed a new inner tube. He set off to push to the nearest village. There'd been one five miles back. Surely the next one must be closer. He went forward. That was his second mistake.

Two hours later and John had still not seen a living human or a house. His feet and legs were thick with mud and the cycle seemed five times heavier than when he'd set out.

He looked up, brushed the rain out of his eyes and saw a lone house. Shelter and warmth, he thought. Not a village with a bicycle repair shop, but a resting place at least. He turned off the muddy lane and headed towards it. That was John's third, and greatest, mistake.

The driveway was overgrown. The late afternoon was dull and dreary, but there were no lights in the windows. The house was large with fine, tall chimneys, yet there was no smoke coming from them. It had clearly been a farmhouse – there were barns and sheds at the side. And it had been a rich farmer's house, for behind it John could see that the gardens had their own lake.

His heart sank. It was obviously deserted now. No warm welcome here. At least, he thought, there'd be shelter. He could dry out and wait for the rain to stop.

He knocked at the heavy front door. The knock boomed through the empty house. He tried the door handle. To his surprise it was unlocked. John stepped into the gloom of the hall and wheeled his cycle in.

"Hello?" he called. There was no reply.

He propped his cycle against the wall and went into the living room. For some reason it was still furnished. The smell of damp and decay was powerful. But the fireplace looked inviting. John ran back through the rain to the barn where he found some scraps of dry wood and straw to make a blaze.

When he returned to the living room he almost dropped his armful of wood in fear. For there, in the dust of the floor, was a trail. It led from the locked french-windows across to the settee. Even in the shadowy room the trail glistened clearly. It was thick, wet slime.

John edged his way around it and placed the wood in the fireplace. His hands trembled as he tried to light a match. At last the fire flared into life. He could see that the trail ended at a sofa. In the flickering light he could now see something lying on the sofa.

He licked the rain off his chin, for his mouth had gone strangely dry. He peered at the rags on the sofa. They were the remains of a pair of pyjamas – muddy and mouldering and stinking. Worse, they made John suddenly afraid. He backed away.

A sudden draught blew out the fire and plunged the room back into its late-afternoon gloom. A sound in the hallway made him grab for a poker. The sound was of something wet and soft falling to the floor.

"Who's there?" John crept to the door and flung it open. Only his dripping cycle stood where he had left it.

He laughed at his own fears, then hurried back to light the fire again. "I'll be all right once I'm warm and dry," he muttered. "But I don't think I'll be staying the night."

Then that weird and chilling sound came from the doorway again. It seemed nearer now! A thick trail of slime was in the passageway. But worse . . . it was moving towards the room!

John backed away. The slime-trail followed him. His back was to the fireplace now but the trail didn't seem to be interested in him . . . yet.

It turned towards the sofa and the ragged pyjamas. As it reached the sofa the pyjamas seemed to jerk into life. First they rose up, lifted by an invisible hand. Then they began to swell out as if they were being filled by a living body. But it was an invisible body and a very wet one, for the pyjamas began to dribble with water.

John didn't wait to see what the pyjamas planned to do next. He ran. He ran through the doorway and through the hall, leaving the cycle behind. He rushed into the streaming rain without noticing it. He stumbled back down the tangled drive and onto the muddy lane.

His head down, he ran blindly into the fading evening shadows. He ran a mile before he came to the village. The local inn was the first building he came to. He burst through the door and stood, wild-eyed and weak-kneed at the bar.

The landlord looked at the Englishman with pity. He guided

him to a seat and pushed a large glass of brandy into his hand. John gulped at it thankfully. Everyone in the bar room was staring at him. In the warmth and light of the inn John suddenly felt his fears had been foolish. "Sorry," he said. "No money! It's with my cycle . . . in a house . . . down the road."

The landlord patted his shoulder. "Oui, monsieur. Tonight, stay here."

"My cycle . . ."

"We will fetch it tomorrow. Tonight you must rest."

"But that house!"

"We know all about the house, monsieur," the landlord said. "But tonight you rest."

In the warm bedroom of the inn, John slept – an exhausted sleep. It was the next morning when he began to unravel the terrible truth behind the farm. John spoke little French and the landlord just a little more English. With the help of three-year-old newspaper cuttings, they pieced together the story.

Just six years before, during the Second World War, the farm had been owned by a strange and lonely man, an artist called Marc Baus. Of course, the German army controlled the country at that time; the French were forced to work for them and obey them. Many brave French people resisted the mighty German army and tried to fight them. Many died in the attempt. Too many. Someone was betraying the French Resistance fighters to the Germans! Everyone in the village suspected Marc Baus.

When the war ended, Baus was brought to trial for his treachery. To the disgust of the villagers he was given just two years in prison. By 1948 he was back at his farm. They remembered the dead and their hatred of Baus boiled up. They marched to the farm and threatened to kill him. Their stones shattered his windows. Only the arrival of the local police saved his life.

But Baus was a frightened and friendless man. He was never seen again . . . alive. Two months after the stoning, his body was found in the little lake behind the house. The police took the dripping body into the house to examine it. The water and slimy weeds trailed across the floor of the living room as they carried it in. They laid the corpse on the sofa. Baus had been wearing pyjamas when he died.

The surgeon announced that he had drowned . . . he was not able to say how. Perhaps it was an accident. Perhaps it was suicide . . . perhaps it was murder of the most hated man in the region. The body was buried in a flowerless grave.

"You were not surprised when I came in last night," John Allen said.

The landlord shook his head. "You are not the first to shelter from a storm in that old house. Two years ago, two workers sheltered there . . . they saw the same as you, monsieur. Now no one ever goes into that house. Some braver men will bring your cycle . . . not me! I would not go near there again. No, not for twenty million francs!"

John nodded. "Nor would I," he shuddered. "Nor would I!"

The haunted farmhouse was demolished to make way for a new motorway. The ghost has not been seen since then.

Ghostly Evidence — FACT FILE

Many ghosts, like the one in the haunted French farmhouse, are said to leave some evidence of their presence other than their appearance . . .

1. **Water** Ghosts that have met watery deaths are said to leave wet footprints or perhaps a trail of slime when they return.

2. **Scent** In Bramshill House at Hartney Wintney in Hampshire, England, a bride with her wedding bouquet played hide-and-seek with her guests after the ceremony. But she became trapped in a chest and suffocated. The scent of her bouquet of lilies still hangs in the air when she appears. Her death is said to have happened in 1725. The house is now a police training establishment.

3. **Sounds** Ghosts are often heard if not seen. People living at the edge of battlefields have claimed to hear the sounds of clashing weapons and screams of the dead for centuries after.

4. **Touch** People who claim to have seen ghosts very often mention a freezing chill that comes with the ghost.

5. One of the most curious watery graves can be found in Massachusetts . . .

Underneath this stone
Lies poor John Round.
Lost at sea
And never found.

(Think about it!)

6. It's reckoned that one person in ten will see a ghost in their lifetime . . . but not everyone will recognize it at the time. There are countless stories of people thinking they'd seen a friend (or relation), then finding out much later that the friend had already died.

7. Children under ten years are more likely to see ghosts than people of any other age. Perhaps as people grow older they are afraid of being laughed at if they claim to have seen one. Or maybe adults try to explain away what they've seen, whereas children just accept it.

T·H·E
BODYSNATCHERS

Some people will do anything to make money. Two hundred years ago they did the most disgusting thing of all . . . they sold dead bodies.

Edinburgh, Scotland – 1827

"Good morning, Mr Desmond. Time to get up!" William Hare was the manager of the old boarding house. He kicked at the old man. Old Desmond didn't move. The only things moving on the filthy, straw-filled mattress were the fleas.

"Come along, Mr Desmond! All the others are out and about, on the streets begging!" Hare giggled. He had never been able to control that giggle. He rubbed his rough hands and looked proudly round the room. It was a good room. Only two metres by three but he'd packed three beds into it. With three men and women to each bed he could make a nice, fat profit from renting the sleeping places.

But he'd never make a profit from the likes of Old Desmond. The man was getting too feeble to beg. He hadn't paid for weeks. William Hare's eyes narrowed. "We don't want to have to put you out on the streets, now do we, Mr Desmond?" he said. The old man didn't reply.

"You owe three pounds already," Hare went on and kicked the man harder. He bent down and shook the pauper. "So get out there and earn it!"

But the old man was stiff and cold.

Hare gave a cry of rage. "Dead! Dead and owes me three pounds!"

The door swung open and a shorter, dark-haired man looked in. "Something wrong, Mr Hare?" William Burke asked. He had a small hammer in his hand and a scrap of leather. He took old shoes, patched them and sold them on the streets. Hare had rented out a tiny room at the back of the house for him to work in.

"Wrong? Aye, there's something wrong. Old Desmond here has died!" Hare snarled.

"May God have mercy on him," Burke murmured.

Hare gave a sudden, wild giggle. "May God have mercy on me!" he screeched. "The man owed me more than three pounds . . . nearly four!"

"That's sad, Mr Hare," Burke agreed. "If you like I'll call on the parish clerk to arrange to have him buried."

William Burke and William Hare got drunk. They sat on the floor of Burke's little cobbler workshop and stared at the rough, wooden coffin.

"Tell me again," Hare said softly. "How can I get my money out of the old man?"

"Sell his body," Burke answered carefully.

"Sell his body," Hare nodded and giggled. "You want to buy it, Burke?"

"No use to me. But they do say that the doctors in the town want bodies . . . and they are willing to pay."

"Four pounds?"

"Four pounds – two for you and two for me," Burke said.

"Can we do that?" Hare asked.

"No," his lodger said. "We can't do it legally. We have to do it secretly."

"But they'll come to bury him tomorrow!" Hare argued.

"We fill his coffin with some of the rubbish from this workshop. No one will ever know."

Hare nodded. "Pass me your hammer, Burke." He took it and began to work at the nails on the lid.

Doctor Knox looked at Burke and Hare with some disgust. "The body is not in perfect condition," he said. "I can only offer you seven pounds!"

Burke's jaw fell in surprise. Hare gave a sudden, wild giggle. "Seven pounds!"

The Doctor misunderstood. He thought the offer was too small. "Very well . . . seven pounds and ten shillings. Not a penny more!"

"We'll take it, sir!" Burke said quickly.

"But take the shirt away," Doctor Knox said angrily.

"The shirt?" Burke gaped. "We don't want it, sir."

"You stupid man!" the doctor exploded. "The body belongs to no living person. It is a crime for you to sell it, but it is not a crime for me to buy it. The shirt is different. The shirt belonged to the old man. I would go to prison if I was caught buying the shirt."

Hare shook his head, confused.

"If you bring me more bodies, bring them without clothes," the Doctor said.

"More?" Burke said sharply. "You want more?"

"We always need more," Doctor Knox said sadly.

"Why . . . sir?" Hare asked with a simpering grin.

"We are a medical school," the doctor explained. "How can we cure the sick if we don't understand how the body works? You wouldn't want us to cut you up while you were alive, would you?" Hare shuddered, shook his head and giggled nervously.

Doctor Knox sighed. "The law will only allow us to use the bodies of dead criminals. There are so precious few of those. Some fellows have taken to digging up bodies from graveyards," he said in a low voice. "Understand, I do not wish to know where you obtain your bodies. Just bring them to me." Suddenly he pointed a thin finger at the men. "You are doing a service to the world of medicine."

"Thank you, sir," Burke smiled.

"Thank you, sir," Hare cringed as they backed towards the door.

The two men slid out into the lampless Edinburgh night.

Burke and Hare were moody and restless. "Seven pounds and ten shillings, spent and gone," Burke groaned.

"Spent and gone," Hare giggled.

"It's a pity old Desmond isn't still with us," Burke sighed.

"Aye, then he could get sick and die again," Hare agreed. The two men sat silent for a while.

"Old Joseph's sick," Burke said softly.

"Sick but not dead," Hare reminded him.

"Aye, not dead . . . yet," Burke said. The silence fell between them like dust settling on the dirty table.

"He'll be dead soon," Burke went on.

"Not soon enough for me," Hare added viciously.

"And not soon enough for Joseph," Burke added gently. "It cannot be pleasant for the poor old soul to suffer like that."

Hare's little eyes glittered as he began to catch his partner's meaning. "Death would be a kindness," he said carefully.

Burke met Hare's eyes. "A kindness. And Joseph's friends would want to be kind to him – help him to die."

"Let him starve," Hare suggested.

"Too slow."

"Poison him?"

"Too painful."

"Wait till he falls asleep . . ."

"And smother him!"

"Pass me that pillow, Burke."

Doctor Knox gave the two men ten pounds for old Joseph's body. He asked no questions and didn't seem to notice how the old man had died. Doctor Knox found they were becoming reliable bodysnatchers. But they weren't bodysnatchers. They were murderers.

They weren't *taking* dead bodies . . . they were *making* dead bodies.

The poor people of Edinburgh kept disappearing, month after month – fourteen . . . fifteen . . . sixteen . . .

Burke and Hare began to lure the weak and the drunken to their lodging house. Sometimes they had unlikely allies in their work. One night, Constable Andrew Williamson found a drunken old woman asleep in the gutter. "Come along, lady, it's off to the jail with you. We'll give you a wooden bed and a cup of cold porridge."

He heaved her to her feet and began to struggle down the street with her. A watching figure slid from the shadows.

"Good evening, Constable Williamson," William Burke said softly.

"Ah!" the young policeman grunted. "Evening, Mr Burke."

"Who have we here?" the bodysnatcher breathed.

"Some old biddy who's got drunk on too much gin."

"Taking her home, are you?" Burke asked.

"To jail," Constable Williamson groaned as he struggled to hold the woman upright.

"Oh, but her family will worry," Burke frowned. "It would be a kindness if you'd let me take her home. I happen to know where she lives."

The young constable brightened. "Why, Mr Burke! It *is* a kindness, that's for sure," he said and passed the mumbling woman to the bodysnatcher.

"Goodnight, Mr Burke," the policeman smiled. "And thank you!"

"No!" Burke chuckled. "Thank *you*!" And he led another victim back to the boarding house.

As she snored on the louse-ridden bed, Burke lay on top of her to pin her arms and legs down. Then Hare placed a huge hand across her mouth and pinched her nose. The old woman struggled under Burke's great weight. She fought for breath. She tried to scream.

After a minute, the struggles grew weaker. A minute later they stopped . . . forever. Like many others she died of suffocation. Before the sun came up next morning, her frail old body was lying in a box in the surgeon's house.

Not all their victims died so easily. One old woman had her deaf-mute grandson with her. They killed the woman and planned to set the poor boy free – after all, he couldn't speak to tell his tale. But the boy was fretting and making a fuss. Burke was worried that somehow he might lead the police back to the boarding house.

He took the boy into the back room and broke his spine across his knee. The bodies were packed in a pickled-herring barrel and taken off to Surgeon's Square.

But Burke and Hare grew greedy. Burke and Hare grew careless. The police received a terrible report. A couple called Grey had stayed in the boarding house and met an old lady called Docherty. The next morning the old lady had vanished. As Mrs Grey cleaned up the bedroom the next day, she saw blood on the straw of the bedding. And under the straw lay a lifeless arm . . . it belonged to the dead Mrs Docherty.

The Greys left the body and Mr Grey went to the police. Constable Fisher investigated. "When did you last see Mrs Docherty?"

"Last night at seven," Burke lied. "She left the house last night and no one's seen her since."

The constable thought that Burke was an honest man. He believed him at first and went in search of Burke's wife. "When did you last see Mrs Docherty?" he asked her.

"Oh, at seven o'clock this morning," she told him. "She spent the night at our house."

Constable Fisher was puzzled. Someone was lying. The old woman's body was found at Knox's surgery. The police doctor examined it. He reported that Mrs Docherty could have been suffocated – but, then again, she could have died of natural causes.

The police were sure that Burke and Hare were guilty of murder. But one dead old woman and a few lies don't make a murder case. What they needed was someone who had seen a murder. A witness.

And a witness did come forward. He had seen Burke commit more than one killing. Who was this witness? Burke's old partner, William Hare! For the frightened Hare had made a deal – the police said that he could go free, but only if he went to court and put the blame on Burke. The cowardly Hare agreed.

On 28 January 1829 William Burke went to the gallows. He was sorry for his crime – but still angry that Knox hadn't paid him in full for that last dead body. The money could have bought him a fine coat for his execution!

The crowd gathered to watch Burke die. They howled their hatred at the man who, they said, had killed thirty harmless people. The rope was short and Burke did not die instantly. As the crowds cheered he died slowly and in agony, gasping for breath . . . just as so many of his victims had done.

And, when he was dead, his body was handed over to the doctors to be cut up for their experiments.

The nineteenth-century streets of Edinburgh were just a little safer.

Bodysnatching – FACT FILE

1. Bodysnatchers usually dug up bodies after they had been buried. Someone who rises from the dead is said to be resurrected. Because they "raised the dead", bodysnatchers were often known as "Resurrectionists".

2. Families tried to protect their dead relatives' coffins by burying them under steel cages so they couldn't be dug up.

3. Some cemeteries had watch-houses built and put guards in with guns. Guards were often nervous, all alone in a graveyard at night. They would often shoot anything that moved. That probably explains how some cemetery guards in Aberdeen once killed a pig.

4. Bodysnatchers could make extra money by selling teeth from bodies to dentists. These teeth would then be used to make false teeth.

5. Bodysnatchers often worked in gangs. They kept some secrecy by using nick-names such as "Lousy Jack", "Praying Howard", "The Spoon" (because of his curious shovel), "The Mole" (because he was such a good digger), "The Screw" and "Merry Andrew".

6. "The Spoon" and "The Mole" were angry with "Merry Andrew" because they felt he'd cheated them of their share of bodysnatching money. When "Merry

Andrew's" sister died they decided to steal and sell her body. "Merry Andrew" guessed their game and let them dig her up. As soon as they had, he leapt out from behind a gravestone with a white sheet over him. They ran away. "Merry Andrew" took his own sister straight to the surgeons and sold her.

7. Two medical students, Henry and George, fell in love with the same girl. She preferred Henry and was heartbroken when he died. She wept over his grave. George was so jealous that he had Henry's body removed and sold. He then enjoyed watching the girl weeping and praying at the graveside. Only *he* knew it was empty soil!

8. Expert bodysnatchers used wooden spades because they were quieter than metal ones.

9. Bodysnatchers were also known as "Sack-'em-up men" because of the way they would dig 'em up, then sack 'em up.

10. Selling bodies to doctors stopped soon after Burke and Hare were caught. The law changed to allow surgeons to have more bodies legally.

DIARY OF A
HORROR
HOUSE

It's America's favourite true horror story with a best-selling book and a popular film based on it.

Amityville, New York, USA – 1965 to 1976

The house at 112 Ocean Avenue is a fine one. It stands on the edge of the Amityville River. It has its own boathouse, heated swimming pool, two-car garage, large living rooms and six bedrooms. It also has a tragic history.

1965 – Ronald DeFeo and his family move into 112 Ocean Avenue, Amityville. Ronald likes the place and puts up a name-board at the end of the garden saying, "High Hopes". The DeFeos are a religious family and there is a model of a religious scene on that lawn. They seem a normal and happy family.

November 1974 – Mr and Mrs DeFeo are still living at 112 Ocean Avenue with their five children. They would be happy if it weren't for the oldest son, Ronnie. Ronnie is spoilt. He has been in trouble with the police on more than one occasion. Ronnie has been charged with theft – even though he has all the money he needs – and with taking drugs. Early this month he is suspected of being mixed up in a $19,000 robbery. This is the last straw. His father throws him out of the house.

13 November 1974 – Ronnie runs into a local bar and cries, "My father and mother have been shot!"

The men from the bar rush to 112 Ocean Avenue and find the whole family in their beds. Each one has been turned face down on their bed and shot with a high-powered rifle. The killer has rested their heads on their arms. The men from the bar call the police.

The police discover that the victims had all been drugged at supper that night. The killer must have done this so he could return and kill them without disturbing anyone. The killer must have been someone very close to the family.

The murder weapon is found. Ronnie is arrested. He is accused of drugging his family so they fell deeply asleep. As they slept, he shot them.

18 November 1974 – Ronnie DeFeo is charged with all six murders.

September 1975 – Ronnie DeFeo comes to trial. It is the longest trial ever held in Amityville. He tries to say the police beat him into confessing and that he didn't really kill his parents. He shows very little regret that his family are dead.

4 December 1975 – The Judge sentences Ronnie DeFeo to 150 years in prison. Ronnie DeFeo finally confesses to the massacre. "It just started," he said. "It went so fast . . . I just couldn't stop."

18 December 1974 – Meanwhile, a new family move into 112 Ocean Avenue – George Lutz and his wife, Kathleen. The children are from Kathleen's first marriage: two boys, Chris and Danny, and a little girl, Melissa – Missy for short.

The Lutzes know about the DeFeo murders – after all, that's how they got the house so cheaply – but they are not too bothered. Just to be safe they have their family priest, Father Frank Mancuso, come in to bless the house.

As Father Mancuso walks through the house sprinkling holy water, a deep voice says, "Get out!" Father Mancuso is puzzled but not worried . . . yet. Later that day his car almost crashes when the bonnet and door fly open. The car cannot be restarted.

He gets a lift from another priest – that priest later has a serious accident.

George Lutz discovers that much of the furniture of the dead DeFeos is in store since the massacre. He agrees to buy it. The house is returning to the way it was at the time of the gruesome murders.

The family dog is chained in a pen outside to guard the house. As darkness falls George hears the dog howling terribly. Something has scared it so badly that it tried to jump out of the pen and has almost strangled itself on the chain. George shortens the chain.

19 December 1974 – The family go to bed and sleep soundly – all except George Lutz, who wakens to an unexplained knocking at a quarter past three in the morning. This was the exact time at which the DeFeo family were murdered in their beds. George looks out of the window. The dog begins to bark furiously at something invisible down by the boathouse. George thinks he can see a shadowy shape vanishing into the boathouse. When he goes to investigate he finds the boathouse door swinging open in the freezing wind, yet he knows he closed it before he went to bed.

20 December 1974 – Things are starting to turn unpleasant for the Lutz family. George is waking at a quarter past three *every* morning. He is becoming short-tempered and hitting the children – something he has never done before. He is going for days without shaving or showering – something else he has never done. He is piling logs on the fire to warm himself during the day. The house is like an oven – but George is freezing.

22 December 1974 – Something strange happens to the toilets when they suddenly turn black with a stain that repeated scrubbing can't quite remove. A sickly-sweet perfume lingers in the air. When George goes to open a window to let out the smell, he sees it is covered with hundreds and hundreds of flies. Other windows are clear, but one window only is black with them. It is the window that faces the boathouse.

That night, at exactly a quarter past three, George is awakened by a crash. He hurries downstairs to find the front door torn open and hanging from one hinge.

24 December 1974 – Christmas Eve and Father Mancuso is ill with a raging temperature. George phones the priest and begins to tell him about the mysterious happenings. As Father Mancuso tries to give George a warning . . . the phone is mysteriously cut off. That evening the flies return to the window facing the boathouse.

George feels an urge to check the boathouse. As he turns back to the house he sees Missy staring out of the window at him. Behind the little girl is the face of a pig looking over her shoulder. The pig's eyes glow red. When he runs to her bedroom he finds the girl asleep.

25 December 1974 – George wakes – again at a quarter past three. His wife, Kathy, is sleeping with her head resting on her arms – just as the dead DeFeos were found. He touches her and she wakes screaming. "She was shot in the head! Mrs DeFeo was shot in the head! I heard the explosion!"

After Kathy has gone back to sleep the dog begins to bark. George slips outside. As he looks back to Missy's bedroom window he sees the little girl looking out at him. And, behind Missy's shoulder, is the face of that same pig staring out with glowing red eyes. When George checks her room, he again finds her lying asleep – face down with her head resting on her arms.

On Christmas Day, Missy begins to talk about her new friend – a pig called Jodie – but her brothers say the pig is just in her imagination. That night Kathy hears Missy talking to someone in her room. "Who are you talking to, Missy? An angel?"

"No, Mom, just my friend Jodie," the little girl tells her.

26 December 1974 – On Boxing Day a guest loses an envelope containing $1500, and the next day the Lutzes discover a hidden room behind a cupboard. The room has a sickly but familiar smell – it is the smell of blood.

Before New Year, George Lutz has begun to investigate the past of the house and its site. The local history association tell him it was near an American Indian camp for the sick, the mad and the dying – but the dead were never buried there because it was infested with demons.

1 January 1975 – Kathy Lutz sees the shape of a demon in the blazing log-fire. And, when the fire has died, the white shape of a horned head can be seen in the black soot of the chimney-back.

That night, a gale blows through the house and rips the bedclothes from George and Kathy's bed. The window facing the boathouse is open.

2 January 1975 – Mysterious footprints appear in the snow by the boathouse – hoofprints of the kind the devil is said to leave.

6 January 1975 – George wakes in the middle of the night. He looks across at his wife – she is not there. He switches on the light and sees her, floating in the air above the bed . . . but her face is that of a ninety-year-old woman. He drags her down by the hair, she awakes, looks at her face in the mirror and screams. Slowly her face returns to almost normal . . . but there are wrinkles in her face that weren't there before.

10 January 1975 – Kathy wakes to find her body covered in scratches. By the evening they have disappeared as mysteriously as they arrived. The curse of living in the house is affecting other parts of the family's life – George's business is heading towards bankruptcy.

11 January 1975 – This is one of the worst days yet. A storm smashes doors and windows while the rain floods in. The storm smashed trees in the garden of 112 Ocean Avenue – but not the trees in the rest of the street.

George and Kathy let the guard-dog into the house to see what it can sense. The dog refuses to go into Missy's room.

12 January 1975 – George wakes from a horrific nightmare. A hooded figure picked him up – the same figure the family had seen burned into the fireplace. The face emerged from the hood and George recognised it. It was his own face, but it was hideously torn in two!

As he woke from the dream, shaken, Missy tells him, "Daddy, come to my room. Jodie wants to talk to you."

"Who's Jodie?"

"Jodie's my friend. The biggest pig you ever saw."

George runs to the room. He can see no pig.

"There he is, Daddy!" Missy cries and points at the window.

Two red eyes stare back in. No pig, not even a face. Just two red eyes.

"That's Jodie," the little girl cries. "He wants to come in!"

Kathy rushes past George, she picks up a chair and hurls it at the window. The window shatters; there is a squealing, pig-like scream of pain and the eyes vanish. There is nothing to be seen when they look through the broken window. But the squealing sound can be heard disappearing towards the boathouse.

13 January 1975 – Missy talks to Jodie under the table at breakfast.

"Who is this Jodie?" Kathy demands.

"He's an angel," Missy says. "He tells me about a little boy who used to live in my room. The little boy died, you know."

Missy's room was one where the DeFeos' young son had been murdered.

"Jodie says he's going to live here forever," Missy says proudly.

This is the final straw for the frightened Lutz family. They are sure that something is sharing the house with them. Something so horrible in smell and clammy touch that they can bear it no longer.

Their priest, Father Mancuso, advises them to "Let whatever's there have the place. Just go."

But, before they can leave, the storms return. The house grows hotter, though the heating is off – all except Missy's room which is freezing. George goes to open a window. He looks with disgust at the playroom door. Something green and slimy appears to be oozing through the door and into the hall. A jelly that has a mind of its own. The green slime begins to slither down the stairs. He manages to stop the flow by blocking the gap with towels.

14 January 1975 – George goes to bed, exhausted by his struggle against the slime. But he wakes to something climbing over his body – something with hooves.

The children wake screaming that some faceless creature has invaded their room. As George goes to investigate he sees that same huge hooded figure, blocking his way. It raises a finger and points at the man.

George gathers his family and orders them to get out. The Lutz family flee their house of horror. They have lived there just twenty-eight days.

George and his family move into the house of Kathy's mother. Peace at last . . . perhaps.

15 January 1975 – George is woken by his wife. "George! You were floating above the bed! We have to get out of this room!" She leads him out onto the landing. They stop. Coming up the stairs towards them is a trail of green-black slime . . .

Amityville – FACT FILE

Is the story true? Or was it invented by the Lutzes to get some publicity and make a lot of money from telling their story? Remember, George's business was failing! These are some of the facts that seem to support George and Kathy Lutz's story . . .

1. After the Lutzes moved out, a new family moved in. The son of the new owners slept in murderer Ronnie DeFeo's bedroom until he died at a tragically early age.

2. Jay Anson wrote a best-selling book on the case and sold the story to the makers of a very popular film. While he was writing the book some eerie things happened.

3. The manuscript of a few chapters was loaned to a woman . . . her house burst into flames and the only thing not damaged was the manuscript.

4. A man was driving with the manuscript in the boot of his car when the car slid into a deep, water-filled hole . . . and the only dry thing to be rescued next day was the manuscript.

5. The completed text was taken to the publisher by car . . . the car caught fire and all the engine bolts were found to be loose.

6. Anson had a heart attack . . .

7. . . . and his son was almost killed in a car crash.

8. A photographer arrived at Jay Anson's house to photograph the author. For some reason his parked car burst into flames.

9. Anson was so famous now that he earned one million dollars for his next book. Shortly after he received the million-dollar cheque, he died of a heart attack.

10. Newspaper writer Paul Hoffman wrote the first article at the time of the strange happenings. He died some time later in strange circumstances.

11. In the film, an actor called James Brolin played the part of George Lutz. He claimed he was hit by bad luck from the moment he started filming. His lift trapped him on the first day. On the second day he had been filming for one minute when he tripped and sprained an ankle. The delays cost the film company a fortune.

12. The film-makers were so scared the story might be true that they refused to use 112 Ocean Avenue for the filming.

On the other hand, many people argue that the Amityville horror is nonsense because . . .

1. There are no witnesses to the strange happenings except for the family and their priest, who was feverish at that time with 'flu.

2. The claims that the house was built on an old Indian camp for the sick, the mad and the dying were simply not true. The Shinnecock Indians who lived in the region before white settlers arrived never had any such camp in any place.

3. The Parapsychology Institute of America (which investigates the supernatural) was called in by George Lutz . . . but then he suddenly cancelled the visit. Was he afraid that his claims would be proved false? The director of the Parapsychology Institute went ahead and personally investigated the house and the claims. He decided that the horror story was simply made up. (By then, of course, it was too popular a story. No one wanted to believe it was a fake!)

4. The next owners of the house, the Cromarty family, made a huge joke of the story. They were pestered by sightseers but didn't mind showing some people round the scenes of so-called horror. They even held Hallowe'en parties to tempt the demons out. Nothing unusual ever happened.

The Lutz family are alive and well. They moved to California where they were planning to write another book about their experiences.

THE GHOST OF THE RED BARN

Can a ghost come back to earth and tell its relatives how it died? Some stories seem to prove that they can . . .

Polstead, Suffolk, England – 1827

The cottage was small, cold and very dark. It smelled of babies and dead moles. Mrs Ann Marten struck a light and lit a candle by the bedside. Her husband, John, snored deeply. "John," she hissed. The man groaned and turned his back to her. The mole-catcher was getting old, deaf and tired.

The woman pulled a shawl around her shoulders and put her lips closer to his ear. "John!" He smiled at some half-remembered dream but didn't wake. Somewhere in the shadows a sleeping child stirred.

Suddenly the chill air was split with a terrified scream. Mrs Ann Marten sat up in bed. A frightened child called out but her husband didn't move. The woman dug a sharp elbow into his ribs. "John, oh, John . . . I've had the most awful dream."

"Go back to sleep," her husband mumbled and blinked in the light of the flickering candle. "It isn't even daylight yet."

"No, John. You have to listen . . . it was a message from beyond the grave!"

The old man rubbed his eyes and struggled to sit up. "What you on about, my love?" he sighed.

"I dreamed about our Maria," she whispered. "She came to me and told me a dreadful story."

"Hah! Well what's all this rot about messages from beyond the grave?" the man grumbled. "Maria's alive and well."

"How do you know?" his wife asked.

"She got married to young William Corder and he took her off to live with him in London. She's safely asleep by now . . . like all good Christians should be," he added.

"No, John," Ann said and shuddered. "In the dream I saw

Maria covered in blood. She tried to speak to me. But all she could say was one word – murdered . . . by Corder!"

"That's three words," the man complained and settled down in the bed again.

"No, listen," the woman urged. "William Corder said he was taking her to London. He said he was going to marry her. But we haven't seen her since that night she left the cottage to meet him in the Red Barn."

"We've had letters," the man argued. But he was wide awake now and frowning.

"Only two or three – and in a strange handwriting," the woman argued.

"Hurt her hand, she said."

"So Corder said. He never wanted to marry our Maria. Him the squire's son and her a poor mole-catcher's daughter. I don't believe he ever went to London with Maria. I always thought that he wrote those letters himself."

The man didn't want to believe her. "So where is Maria if she's not in London with Corder?" he grumbled.

"If my dream were true then he . . . he murdered her!" the woman moaned.

"And what did he do with the body?" the old man asked and shivered again.

"I saw that in my dream too. He buried her in the Red Barn," Ann said. "I saw it in my dream. He murdered her and now her ghost is wandering the earth looking for justice."

"Who'll believe your word against the squire's son?" the man sighed. "What can you do?"

"Nothing," Ann sniffed. "Nothing a poor woman can do alone. But I did think you could go to the Red Barn and look."

The old man rubbed his eyes wearily. "First thing in the morning – well, second thing. Got to catch moles on the squire's orchard first thing. I'll do it second thing in the morning," he promised and turned over.

"No, John. Now!" the woman begged. "I'll never sleep again until I know."

"Dang me! I suppose that means I won't get any sleep either," the man grumbled as he fumbled in the dark for his trousers. He pulled on an old jacket and left the room. He paused at the front door to pick up his mole spud – a sharp wooden stake which he used to kill troublesome moles.

Within half an hour he'd gathered a group of villagers together and with lanterns and spades they set off for the old Red Barn on the top of the hill. With the owls screeching in the woods and the ragged black clouds drifting over the sickle moon, the idea of ghosts seemed more likely now. The villagers were a silent, frightened group as they tugged open the huge brown doors. Not a red barn at all – just a name given to it because of the way it caught the blood-red rays of the setting sun some evenings.

The barn was empty of hay at this time of the year. Another few weeks and the harvest would fill it. The lanterns on the floor caught the red eyes of the angry rats who squeaked and scuttled out of sight.

The floor was hard-packed earth. Too hard to dig it all. Men moved forward and prodded the ground with spades. Old John Marten used his mole spud – the spike clacked time and again against the hard floor. Then suddenly, the spud sank into a soft patch. "Ah!" the man gasped. He pulled out the spike. There was something sticky and evil-smelling on the end.

He stared at it. The villagers gathered around. "You want to go home while we dig?" one of the men asked.

The old man shook his head. Carefully the villagers scraped away the soft soil. The rats returned to watch curiously, their red eyes glinting in the lantern light. The shovels scraped away a crust of earth. Men knelt to scoop away the soft under-soil with their bare hands.

"Never did trust that William Corder," a woman muttered.

"Eyes too close together," her friend agreed. "A sure sign of wickedness . . . what's that?" she gasped and held her lantern to the ground.

"A scarf!" the man who was lifting soil out said as his hand tangled in a piece of fine material.

At last old John Marten spoke in a hoarse, agonised voice. "That's the scarf Maria was wearing the night she left!"

Someone led him away. They knew that Maria was still wearing that scarf. She had been buried with it round her neck.

"Just like Ann Marten's dream," a woman sighed. "God moves in mysterious ways."

"Amen," the villagers muttered as they slowly uncovered the body of poor Maria Marten. As they dragged the body clear of the shallow grave they found something else – a pistol. One of a pair of pistols. And the other belonged to William Corder.

Corder was traced to London and arrested. The trial was a sensation. The story of Maria Marten's murder in the Red Barn was turned into a play. Actors showed Corder killing Maria before the man had even been found guilty.

But the greatest sensation in the court and on the stage was Mrs Ann Marten's dream. It was a miracle. The ghost had returned to tell her mother of her murder. The body had been found where the ghost said it would be. Maria had returned from the grave to ask for justice and revenge.

If so, then she got it. Corder was hanged in front of a crowd of ten thousand people. That play, *Maria Marten* – or *The Murder in the Red Barn*, is still performed today.

Is this proof that ghosts really exist . . .?

Ghost of The Red Barn – FACT FILE

1. Mrs Ann Marten wasn't Maria's mother. She was her stepmother, married to Maria's old father. Ann Marten wasn't much older than her step-daughter. When Maria was alive they argued bitterly. Why didn't the ghost appear in the dreams of her true blood relation, her father?

2. One night in 1826 Maria told Mrs Marten that she was leaving to marry Corder. The next morning, Mrs Marten saw William Corder going towards the Red Barn with a pick-axe and a spade. Later that day Ann Marten asked Corder, "Where is Maria?" Corder replied, "She has gone to London to prepare for our wedding." Mrs Corder said this at the trial. But no one asked why Ann Marten wasn't suspicious then!

3. William was writing letters to the Martens pretending they were written by Maria. But he was also enclosing money in the letters. Why?

4. When the letters and the money stopped coming, Mrs Ann Marten had her amazing dream. Why did the "ghost" wait a year to appear?

Here's an explanation that fits the "facts" as we know them . . .

1. Ann Marten was glad to see the back of Maria. She packed her off to meet Corder at the Red Barn at midnight. She didn't care if Maria lived or died – why should she?

2. The next day she saw Corder with the pick-axe and spade and knew what had happened. Corder never wanted to marry the girl – he was a rich squire's son; she was a peasant – she could never mix in his society. But Maria was blackmailing him into marrying her – she was having his baby and that was not only a disgrace to Corder, it was also against the law if he failed to marry her. Mrs Marten must have known this. Mrs Marten didn't report her suspicions to the law officers – there was money to be made out of blackmailing Corder herself. "Pay me or I'll have the Red Barn searched."

3. Corder went to London and faithfully paid the blackmail. But after a while he grew careless. He stopped paying and thought he was safe.

4. Mrs Marten must have been furious. She couldn't go to the officers and say, "Corder's a murderer but he's been paying me to keep quiet," or she'd be hanged too.

5. She needed a good story that would uncover the crime but keep her part in it hidden. What better than the story of a ghostly dream?

A good story. But a "ghost" story? What do you think?

Ghost-hunters take note. Some people who say they've seen a ghost are telling a lie – even under oath in a murder trial. So, don't believe everything you hear.

Five Ways of Becoming a Ghost

1. Die without a proper burial. Without a proper burial you cannot rest in peace and are forced to wander the earth until your remains are laid to rest. Such ghosts are often heard to moan about their fate and, it is said, have to wait about nine hundred years if no one helps them.

2. Be a murder victim. Then you are compelled to haunt your killer or wander round and tell the world of your end until justice is done. Once your victim is caught and punished you can rest in peace.

3. Be thoroughly evil. If you're wicked on earth then you won't get into a respectable afterlife. You can hang around in "limbo" – neither life nor afterlife – until you have suffered enough for the evil you did when you were alive.

4. Listen out for your family calling you back. After you have gone to the afterlife your family may want to call you back. If the family uses a suitable "medium" (a person who has a "spirit" friend in the afterlife), then you may be recalled to earth to talk to your loved ones.

5. Die suddenly. If you are alive one moment then suddenly dead the next, you may not realise that you have died. Your spirit wanders round trying to carry on as if nothing has happened. It doesn't notice the body being carted off and may wonder why people run away when it approaches. Some battlefields are believed to be haunted by ghosts of this sort.

T·H·E
WITCH'S
EXECUTION

Charles Walton was a strange old man. But did he deserve to die so horribly? And who killed him? And why could Britain's best detective not bring the killer to trial?

Lower Quinton, Warwickshire, England – 14 February 1945

"So what was the strangest case you ever investigated, Superintendent?" a young reporter asked.

The old policeman chuckled. "Ex-superintendent," he said. "I'm retired now."

Gillian Clifford leaned forward. She urged, "You'll always be the most famous detective in England, Superintendent. Everyone's heard of Fabian of the Yard. The cases you solved . . ."

"And the ones I didn't solve," Robert Fabian nodded.

"Like the Lower Quinton witch murder?" the girl said eagerly. "What's the truth about that?"

The retired policeman shook his head. "I can't tell you."

The girl's eyes grew large. "But you know?"

"I have no proof . . . you can't print my thoughts," he smiled.

The reporter closed her notebook. "I won't print anything. But I'd love to know. Tell me. Please."

The man sighed. He sucked on a cold pipe and looked out of the window into the winter-grey sky. "It was this time of year. Saint Valentine's day . . . but it wasn't a day for love. It was a day for death."

"And witchcraft," the girl reminded him.

"So they said. That was because of the old story, of course. Back in 1875 a man killed an old woman by pinning her to the ground with a pitchfork. He cut the sign of the cross into her throat. He said she was a witch and he had to kill her. That was just a few miles away from Lower Quinton."

"And you think Charles Walton was a witch and that was why he was killed in the same way seventy years later in 1945?" the reporter asked.

"I think nothing of the kind, young lady," Robert Fabian frowned. "I believe we were meant to think that!"

He closed his eyes and remembered. "Charles Walton was a strange old man. A bit of a loner, they said. Lived with his niece, Edith Walton. Hobbled around with a walking stick but he was still fit enough to work as a hedge-cutter when the weather was good enough."

"But he did claim to be a witch, didn't he?" the girl asked.

Fabian sucked the pipe again. "When he'd had a bit too much cider he said silly things . . . he claimed to be able to talk to animals!"

"Cider's a witch's brew, isn't it?" the girl asked.

Fabian of the Yard snorted. "I just deal in facts, Miss Clifford. What I discovered was that he had no enemies in the village. I learned that he set out from his cottage that Valentine's morning to cut the hedges of farmer Albert Potter. He had a pitchfork, a bill-hook for chopping the hedge . . . and his walking stick, of course. He told Edith that he'd be home about four."

"And that was the last time he was seen alive?"

"Not quite. Farmer Albert Potter said he saw someone cutting hedges at noon. He said the hedge-cutter was Charles Walton. The hedge-cutter was about a quarter of a mile from the farmhouse," Fabian said carefully.

"A quarter of a mile? Potter must have had good eyes!" the girl gasped.

"Potter said he saw the man's shirt sleeves as the man cut the hedge." Fabian stopped. He raised one eyebrow. "Old Charles Walton had been wearing a shirt with no sleeves."

"So Potter had seen the murderer!" the young reporter said

excitedly. The old policeman didn't reply. He simply looked out of the window and waited. Gillian frowned. What other explanation was there? Slowly she said, "Or Potter was lying?"

Fabian shrugged. "You can say that. I couldn't. Not without proof. But the facts were that Edith arrived home at six o'clock from work. The house was cold and dark and Uncle Charles was missing. She was worried straight away. She called on a neighbour, Harry Beasley, and they set off with a torch to Potter's farm. Potter told them where he'd seen the hedge-cutting going on and led them to the field. When they reached an old willow tree Potter stopped. He told Edith not to come any closer. Charles Walton was lying there . . . dead."

"Killed just like that old woman seventy years before," Gillian Clifford murmured. "A pitchfork pinning him to the ground and a sign of the cross cut into his throat." Suddenly a thought struck the reporter. "How old was Walton when he died?"

The policeman smiled. "Seventy-four."

"So he'd have been about four when the old witch was murdered. He must have known about it!" the girl said.

Fabian nodded. "That's what makes a good detective, Miss Clifford. Asking the right questions – making the right links. Of course, you're right! We checked back in the old police records for 1885 when Charles Walton was a boy." He paused.

"And you found something, didn't you!" Gillian cried.

"Nothing that helped us find his murderer," the ex-policeman sighed. "But something strange, I admit." He sucked on his pipe thoughtfully. "We discovered that a ploughboy had reported seeing a phantom black dog in the area. He'd seen it nine nights in a row on his way home from work . . ."

"And nine's the devil's number," the reporter put in.

"So they reckon," the man agreed. "On the ninth night the dog turned into a headless woman – the next day the ploughboy's sister, a fit and healthy woman, suddenly dropped dead."

"The black dog was a sign of a death in the family! A popular superstition. But what has that to do with Charles Walton?" she asked.

The ploughboy who reported the black dog was Charles Walton," Fabian said quietly.

"So he was into witchcraft!" the girl insisted.

The man shrugged. "All I know is that the stories scared the local people – especially when we found a black dog hanging from a tree near the site of the murder."

"So you found nothing?"

"We found no reason why Charles Walton had to die. No one seemed to have a motive to kill a quiet old man. We did find fingerprints on the handle of the pitchfork – they belonged to farmer Albert Potter. He said he'd tried to pull the fork from the body when he found it . . . but it wouldn't come out."

"Surely he could have managed!" Gillian frowned.

Fabian leaned forward and pointed at the girl with the stem of his pipe. "Miss Clifford, it took two strong policemen to remove that pitchfork. It had gone clean through Charles Walton and deep into the ground."

Gillian shuddered. "So it had to be someone strong. His niece couldn't have done it? I mean, she'd be the one to get his cottage when he died, wouldn't she?"

The man shook his head. "She was at work all day . . . and you're right. It took someone very strong, almost certainly a man."

"Did Walton have any money?" the girl asked suddenly.

"Well, he was very careful with money. He had a bit tucked away. But he wouldn't have had any on him when he was killed. All he had was a pocket watch. And that was missing."

"He wouldn't have been killed for a pocket watch," the reporter said.

"No. And that was found in Walton's garden years later. No, we couldn't find a motive that would hold up in court. That legend of the black dog scared everyone into silence. We got no real help from the villagers, and after a police car knocked over and killed a black dog, people were afraid to help. Seemed we were cursed. Some of them became quite ill after we visited them!" the ex-policeman grumbled.

"So you still say the case had nothing to do with witchcraft?"

"I do know that I was near the scene of the murder one day when a large black dog ran past me. A farm boy appeared straight after. I asked him if he was looking for his black dog. He nearly choked with fright and ran away," Fabian said, slowly shaking his head.

"So who did it, superintendent?" Gillian asked.

He leaned forward again. "Work it out. Who could have done it?"

The reporter frowned. "Farmer Albert Potter," she said. "But what was his motive?"

"We'll come to that in a moment. Just tell me how he could have done it and I'll tell you why he'd want to do it."

Gillian nodded. "Walton was working in Potter's fields. Potter knew he was there because he told the inquest. But he couldn't have seen him a quarter of a mile away. He saw him close to . . . and thought up the story about the shirt sleeves." She paused. "He killed Walton with the pitchfork . . . he was a farmer so he'd probably be strong enough to pin him down like that. Potter went back to his farm. Walton's niece called at Potter's farm later that night and Potter led them straight to the body. And, of course, Potter's fingerprints were on the pitchfork."

Fabian smiled. "Very good. Not enough to charge the man,

but enough to suspect him."

"And the motive?"

"Only suspicion there. No proof at all. But remember old Walton's bit of money he had tucked away. I can tell you that Potter's farming business was not doing well at the time of the murder . . . and he was fond of gambling on the horses. He was definitely short of money. Edith Walton reckoned that Uncle Charles had loaned a lot of money to Potter – all cash, of course. No proof of the loans once Walton was dead."

"I see!" Gillian said eagerly. "On the day of the murder Walton went round to Potter's farm to cut hedges and to ask for some of his money back. The two men argued. Potter didn't have the money. They fought. Potter snatched the pitchfork and killed old Walton!"

"So why would he cut a cross in his throat after the old man was dead?" Fabian asked.

The reporter closed her eyes and tried to concentrate. "When Charles Walton was dead, Potter remembered the old legend of the witch-killing. He didn't want people to look for a real murder motive like money. He wanted to fool the police into looking for a witch-craft murderer!"

"Very good, Miss Clifford. Of course we can't prove any of it. And while Potter's still alive, *you* can't write what we think. But I'm absolutely certain that old Walton wasn't the victim of black magic or black dogs. It was something much simpler – and much more boring, I'm afraid."

The reporter nodded. "Plain and simple greed."

Valentine's Day Murder – FACT FILE

1. Warwickshire had a reputation for witchcraft in the 16th and 17th centuries.

2. An old legend tells of a Warwickshire hill, Meon Hill, being the work of the Devil. The Devil took a huge clod of earth and threw it at a new abbey in Evesham in the eighth century. Saint Egwin used prayer to protect the abbey and the clod fell short. It became Meon Hill. The body of old Charles Walton was found at the foot of Meon Hill.

3. The appearance of a black dog is a sign of the Devil being in the area. Some people believe that the Devil can take the shape of a black dog.

4. The cross shape (cut into the throat) was a Christian sign to stop the Devil from raising a witch from the dead.

5. The iron of the pitchfork was considered a strong magic force which kept evil spirits away from the body. By pinning the "witch" to the ground those evil spirits couldn't fly off with the body.

A DREAM OF
DEATH

Usually, sudden, violent death comes as a complete surprise – but sometimes the victim simply knows how he will die . . .

Washington DC, USA – 14 April 1863

President Abraham Lincoln should have been the happiest man in the USA. For years, the war between the Northern states and the Southern states had raged. Now it was all but over, yet Lincoln was strangely sad.

He sat with his wife Mary and his friend Ward Hill Lamon drinking tea late one night. "You're in a serious mood tonight, Abraham," Lamon said.

The President nodded slowly. The years of struggle had weakened him. He was thin and frail. His black hair and beard straggled untidily. "It's strange how much there is written in the Bible about dreams."

The President leaned forward and rested his elbows on his knees. "If we believe the Bible then we must accept that, in the old days, God and his angels came to people in their sleep and gave them messages through their dreams. Today people think that dreams are foolish."

He fell silent and his dark, sunken eyes stared at the carpet.

"So do you believe in dreams?" Mary asked quietly.

After a while her husband answered. "I can't say that I do . . . but I had one the other night that has haunted me ever since."

Mary Lincoln was a short, plump woman who was usually pale. Now she turned a ghostly white. "You frighten me! What was that dream?"

The tall man sighed and twisted his long, thin hands as he told of his dream. "About ten days ago I went to bed very late. I was exhausted and soon fell into a deep sleep and then began to dream. And in the dream there seemed to be a death-like stillness all around me. Then I heard sobbing as if a number of people were weeping. I dreamed I left my bed and wandered downstairs.

"There I heard the same pitiful sobbing, but the people who were crying seemed to be invisible. I wandered from room to room but there was no living person in sight, only the mournful sounds of distress as I passed along. It was light in all the rooms. I recognised each room, but where were all the people who were grieving as if their hearts would break?

"I was puzzled and worried. What could be the meaning of all this? I walked on until I reached the East Room, which I entered. There I met with a sickening surprise. In front of me was a coffin, and in it was a corpse dressed in burial clothes – its face covered. Around the coffin were soldiers who guarded it; there was a crowd of people, some gazing mournfully at the corpse, and some weeping pitifully.

"I asked one of the soldiers who the dead person was. He told me it was the President, and he had been killed by an assassin! There came a loud burst of crying from the crowd which woke me from my dream. I slept no more that night and, though it was only a dream, I have been strangely troubled ever since." The President fell silent. The story was over.

"That's horrid!" Mary gasped. "I'm glad I don't believe in dreams or I'd be in terror for ever more!" and she hurried off to the comfort of her bed.

But Lamon lingered. "Abraham, perhaps you should be more careful. Don't go out after dark, not even with a guard."

The President gave a weary smile. "Why would anyone wish to assassinate me? And if he did then he could do it any time, day or night, if he was ready to die in the attempt. It is nonsense! What man would be ready to give his life for mine?"

John Wilkes Booth was perhaps the most famous actor in America at that time. Tall, handsome and popular, Booth loved acting and all the fame that went with it. But it still wasn't enough. Booth wanted a greater fame. He wanted fame that would last forever. He wanted to be remembered for some great deed, and remembered long after he was dead.

John Wilkes Booth lived in the Northern states but, during the war, his support was for the Southern states where he'd been born. One man had brought the war about and Wilkes Booth hated him like poison; one man had been to blame for the defeat of the South and Wilkes Booth hated him so much he wanted to kill him . . . even if it cost him his own life! That one man was Abraham Lincoln.

Wilkes Booth plotted and planned but not many men were as willing to risk their lives to see Lincoln dead. He knew he would have to carry out the assassination alone. Still, one man should not have been able to murder a well-guarded President. He would need a lot of luck.

The people wanted to see the President who had helped them win the war. The President didn't much enjoy the theatre, but a visit would make his wife happy and please the people who wanted him to appear in public. He decided to visit Ford's Theatre to see a comedy play.

The President wouldn't sit with the crowds in the ordinary seats. He would sit in the best seats in Ford's Theatre – a box at the side of the stage.

It was private; he could only be seen from the audience if he leaned forward. It was safe; the back door to the box should be locked, and to reach that door a killer would have to pass through a white door which would be guarded by an armed policeman.

John Wilkes Booth was an actor, so he knew Ford's Theatre like he knew his own home. The loathsome President Lincoln was going to walk straight into the killer's chosen den. That afternoon he began his planning.

First, the play. Booth walked into the theatre. "Good afternoon," the stage-hands whispered, pleased to see the famous man. They led him to a seat where he could watch the actors practising.

Booth watched the play and took note of the time as each scene came and went. Actor Henry Hawk was on stage. Alone on stage. Booth reckoned this would be a good time to kill the President. Afterwards, he could jump from the President's box, run across the stage, and only Henry Hawk would stand between him and freedom.

Booth looked at his watch. The play had run for two and a quarter hours. When the real performance was on that night then this scene would be playing at a quarter past ten. That was the time that the President would die.

Henry Hawk looked off the side of the stage and called after a fussy old character, "You sockdologising old mantrap!" That line would get a good laugh.

No one noticed as Booth slipped from his seat and wandered up the stairs and towards the empty box seats. He went through the white door. He found a piece of wood and made it fit between the white door and the wall behind. Once he'd escaped through there, the spar would jam the door shut.

He tried the door to the President's box, looking closely at the lock. It was broken! Booth couldn't believe his luck.

The actor took a small penknife out of his pocket and bored a hole in the door to the box. From there he could see the back of the chair where the hated Lincoln would sit. The President's special chair – a rocking-chair.

He stood in the shadow at the back of the box and watched the actors rehearsing. The stage was just three metres below. An easy jump to freedom.

John Wilkes Booth walked out of the theatre. All he had to do was wait.

Darkness began to fall. Lincoln left for the theatre. As his daytime guard, Crooks, left the White House Lincoln said, "Goodbye, Crooks." The guard wondered why the President had said "Goodbye" and not "Goodnight".

The night guard arrived, late as usual. And a hundred miles to the south of Washington, Ward Hill Lamon looked up at the gloomy sky and worried about his friend the President.

He hoped that Lincoln would take notice of his warning and not go out. Lamon suddenly remembered another strange vision that Lincoln once had. The President had been lying on a couch when he glanced up at a mirror. He saw two reflections: one bright and glowing, the other ghastly as death. "I see the meaning, Lamon. I will have two periods of office as President. The first will be healthy but death will come before the end of the second."

Tonight Lincoln was nearing the end of his second period in office. Lamon shuddered. He would never forgive himself if anything happened to his friend while he was away.

As the clocks crept round to a quarter past ten, the moon rose. Farmers in the western states swore that when the moon rose that night it was the colour of blood.

John Wilkes Booth walked through the front entrance to the theatre.

"Ticket, please?" the sleepy booking clerk asked.

Booth put on a joking act of shock. "You will not want a ticket from me!"

The clerk recognised the great actor and grinned. "Sorry, Mr Booth. Go on in!"

The actor had a small, one-shot pistol up his sleeve and a large knife in his belt.

He climbed the stairs and practised the most important line he had ever had to learn. The line that would tell the guard at the white door this lie: "Message for the President!"

Booth came slowly down the side steps of the darkened theatre, the steps that led to the President's box. He reached the white door. The guard's chair stood empty. Police Officer John F Parker had been there until ten o'clock. He hadn't been able to see the play from there and had grown bored. He left the theatre at the interval and went to a local inn for a drink. The police officer never returned.

So Booth's luck was in. He didn't need his well-rehearsed words. He opened the white door and wedged it shut behind him with the piece of wood. Booth crept to the door of the box and put an eye to the hole he had bored in the corner. Actors' voices drifted up from the stage below. As he grew used to the dimness of the box he could make out the rocking-chair. And the shape of the detested Lincoln's head appeared above the high back.

Booth's hand reached for the pistol. With his other hand he slowly turned the handle of the unlocked door and slid through as silently as settling dust. The President's head was a metre away. The assassin in the shadows raised the pistol. As the hand with the pistol came ever closer, the President's eyes were fixed on the stage. One by one the actors and actresses made their exits. Finally, only Harry Hawk was left.

On stage the actor cried, "You sockdologising old mantrap!"

They were the last words the sixteenth President of the United States ever heard. The audience roared with laughter . . . so loud it drowned the roar of John Wilkes Booth's pistol. The single bullet smashed into the President's head. It entered just behind his left ear and came to rest behind his right eye.

"Revenge for the South!" Booth cried.

Mrs Lincoln turned and looked at the handsome young man who'd appeared in her box. She wondered why her husband didn't move. Slowly the cloud of gunsmoke drifted towards her and the gaslights of the stage glinted on the killer's knife.

Over the screams of laughter from the audience came the screams of Mary Lincoln. The President's dream of death had come true.

Booth jumped onto the stage and broke his leg. He managed to escape but was later found hiding in a barn. He was shot.

"What man would be ready to give his life for mine?" President Lincoln had wondered. The answer was John Wilkes Booth.

Lincoln was carried from Ford's Theatre to a house across the road. He died the next morning.

The Assassination of Lincoln – FACT FILE

Almost a hundred years later, President John Kennedy was shot by an assassin. Many people see startling similarities between the two assassinations.

1. President Lincoln was succeeded by his Vice-President – a man called Johnson . . . President Kennedy was succeeded by *his* Vice-President – a man called Johnson.

2. Lincoln's killer, John Wilkes Booth, had a name of three words with fifteen letters in all . . . Kennedy's killer, Lee Harvey Oswald, also had a name of three words with fifteen letters in all.

3. Lincoln died by a bullet in the back of the head as he sat next to his wife in the Ford Theatre . . . Kennedy died by a bullet in the back of the head as he sat next to his wife in a Ford car.

4. Lincoln's killer shot the President in a theatre and hid in a storeroom (a barn) . . . Kennedy's killer shot the President from a storeroom and hid in a theatre.

The Legend of Lincoln – FACT FILE

Lincoln's dream of death was reported by Lamon as a miraculous warning – but Lamon did not tell this story until some time after the assassination. Over the years many stories grew up around Lincoln and his links with the supernatural. It is said that . . .

1. Lincoln went to a spiritualist who was in touch with the dead. It was she who told him that the spirits wanted him to free the slaves in the Southern states. He took her advice and it was this action that started the American Civil War.

2. A woman went to a spiritualist photographer. His business was taking pictures of the living which turned out to have images of the dead on them after they had been developed. When the woman's picture was printed, the image of Abraham Lincoln appeared to be looking over her shoulder. The woman then revealed her true name – Mary Lincoln, the President's widow! BUT . . . the photographer, Mumler, was later accused of being a trickster! Some of his photos were shown to be fakes.

3. There have been many reports of Lincoln's ghost being seen in the White House over the years.

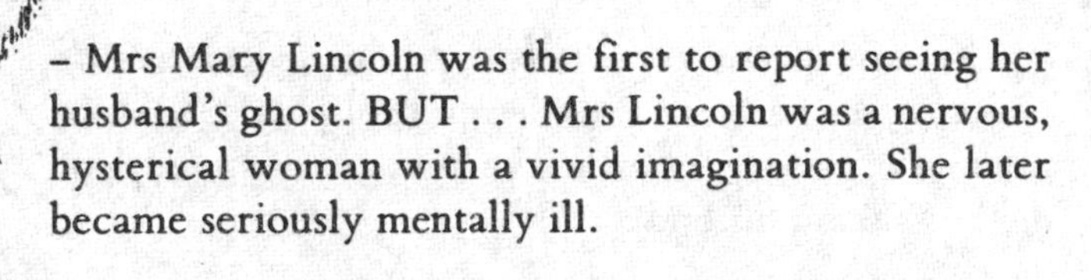

– Mrs Mary Lincoln was the first to report seeing her husband's ghost. BUT . . . Mrs Lincoln was a nervous, hysterical woman with a vivid imagination. She later became seriously mentally ill.

– Queen Wilhelmina of the Netherlands was staying at the White House when she heard a knocking at the bedroom door. She opened it and fell to the floor in a faint. She later told President Roosevelt that she had seen the figure of President Lincoln standing there.

– President Roosevelt never saw the ghost himself but once said that when he was alone in the Blue Room he could often feel the comforting presence of Lincoln's spirit.

– President Harry H Truman said that he had been woken several times by a rapping on his bedroom door while he was at the White House. Truman, unlike Queen Wilhelmina, never saw a ghost.

– Lincoln's appearances have often been announced by a loud, booming laugh for which he was famous.

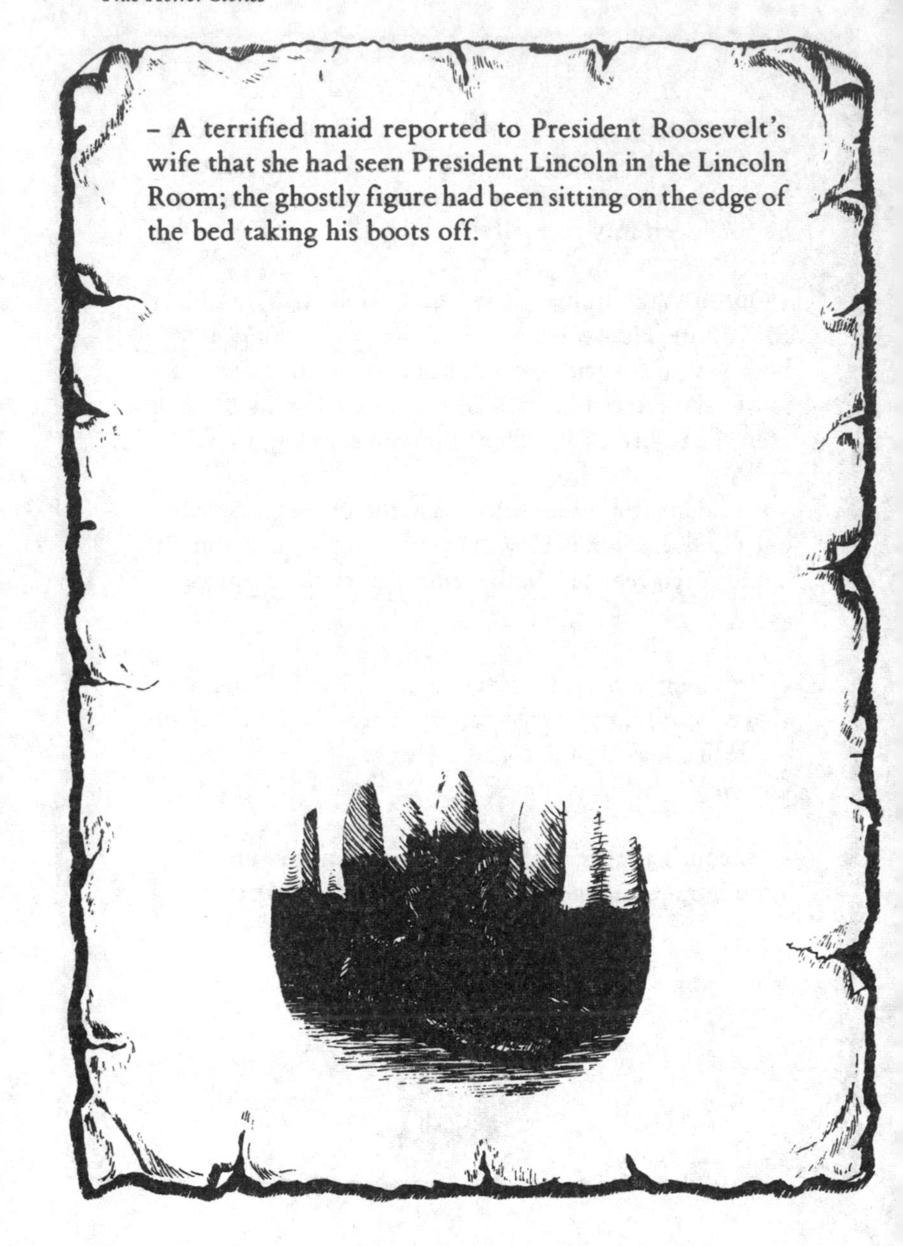

– A terrified maid reported to President Roosevelt's wife that she had seen President Lincoln in the Lincoln Room; the ghostly figure had been sitting on the edge of the bed taking his boots off.

T·H·E
GHOST IN·THE
L·I·F·T

Can a ghost see into the future and warn you of a disaster? Some people believe so. And for many years this story has gone around which seems to prove it.

County Offaly, Ireland – 1883

Lord Dufferin led a busy life, travelling the world in the service of his country. He'd completed six years as the Governor-General of Canada. But now he needed a break.

He had to write a report – an important report for the British government. So he decided that a trip to Ireland would give him the peace he needed. He didn't get it – instead he got something much more valuable. An experience that would save his life ten years later.

Lord Dufferin was tired. The great house near Tullamore in Ireland was silent now – even the servants had gone to bed. He took the candle he'd been working by and lit his way to bed. Not long after he laid his head on the pillow, he drifted into a calm, deep sleep. Until . . .

He awoke with a start. Lord Dufferin didn't know what had woken him. He only knew that it was terrifying. A dream? No, it wasn't a dream. A noise! That was it. He'd been woken by a noise. As he strained his ears he heard it again. And this time he wasn't dreaming. A noise outside on the lawn. The jangle of a horse's harness and the creak of a carriage wheel. But the sound that had chilled him was the soft wailing that was half-human, half-animal.

He was suddenly wide awake – and terrified.

A horse and carriage had no right to be clattering over the lawn of the great house. It belonged on the drive at the front. And what was it doing there in the middle of the night?

In the dim glow of his night-light he found his slippers and tiptoed over to the window. Moon shadows drifted over the silver-green lawn. And from the shadows a man staggered. Staggered under the weight of a huge box on his back.

Lord Dufferin threw open the window to ask the man what was going on. At that moment he realised that the box on the man's back was no ordinary box . . . it was a coffin. He ran across to the man and called him to stop. The stranger raised his head and glared.

"What are you doing here? And what's in that box?" demanded Lord Dufferin.

The stranger's face twisted into an evil leer of pure hated, but he stayed silent. After a few moments he turned to walk back to his carriage.

"Stop!" Lord Dufferin cried and ran after the man, snatching at his arm. But Lord Dufferin's hand seemed to pass clean through that arm.

The stranger threw the coffin onto the carriage where another coffin lay. There was a space left on the carriage wide enough for a third coffin. The strange man turned and snarled at Lord Dufferin. He spoke for the first and only time. "Room for one more, sir, room for one more."

His Lordship boldly ran to grab the man and force him to explain. As he did so the man vanished into the moonlit air. Still shaking, Lord Dufferin returned to his room and made careful notes of what he had seen.

Next morning he read the notes over breakfast to some of his friends who lived locally. "Never been a report of a ghost in this house before," he was told.

"And there's no one in Tullamore who fits the description of this man," someone added with a shake of the head.

"Perhaps it really was just a nightmare. You're over-tired from all that work," a kind friend suggested. "Forget it."

And in time that's just what Lord Dufferin did. Pushed it to the back of his mind, got on with his important work and forgot the man with the coffin.

Almost . . .

Ten years passed. Lord Dufferin became Ambassador to France. He was invited to a glittering reception at the Grand Hotel in Paris.

When he arrived he found the hotel was crowded. And the reception was on the top floor of the hotel. The lifts were very popular that day.

"You could always walk up the stairs," a friend told him.

"Four flights!" Lord Dufferin gasped. "At my age? No," he chuckled. "I'll just be patient and wait for this lift," he said, joining the queue.

The doors slid open and the guests streamed forwards. The lift was full in seconds.

"Better luck next time," someone sighed.

And next time the lift arrived there was indeed a space. The lift looked full so Lord Dufferin stepped back. But the lift attendant thrust his head around the door and looked the ambassador in the eye.

Lord Dufferin stepped back with a cry as he saw the man. The same ugly, evil face of the man he'd seen carrying a coffin in that vision just ten years before."Room for one more, sir," the lift man leered. "Room for one more."

Lord Dufferin shook his head dumbly and staggered back to a chair where he shook with the same fear that had shaken him all those years ago. Weakly, he pushed himself to his feet and walked across to the manager's office.

"Can I have a word?" he asked politely. He didn't know what he wanted to say. Some sort of question about the man . . . or perhaps some sort of warning.

"Of course, monsieur," the manager smiled. "How can I help you?"

As Lord Dufferin struggled to find the right words a waiter rushed through the door and yelled. "Come quickly!" he panted. "The lift!"

"The lift? What's wrong with the lift?" Lord Dufferin whispered.

"Oh, monsieur! The cable snapped when it reached the top. It crashed back down. We fear the people are all dead."

And Lord Dufferin knew that, but for that night at Tullamore, he too would have been a victim of that lift disaster. The vision had saved his life.

The Ghost in the Lift – FACT FILE

1. Lord Dufferin held his title from 1862 until he died in 1902.

2. The first published report of Lord Dufferin's ghost in the lift story did not appear till 1920 – eighteen years after his death and twenty seven years after the supposed crash. Why did the world have to wait so long to hear this incredible story? If it were true then it would have been a newspaper sensation back in 1893, wouldn't it?

3. A lift accident did occur in the Grand Hotel . . . but that was in 1878 – five years before Lord Dufferin's dream and fifteen years before the story says it happened. When the accident did happen there was no reception at the hotel, Lord Dufferin was in Canada at the time – and only one lady died. There is no report of an accident in 1893. How do these facts tie in with the story?

4. The writer of the first story had the facts told to him shortly after his story appeared in print. He never bothered to change the story, however, and many people have retold the same story without bothering to mention the mistakes. Why didn't the 1920 writer bother to check the facts before he printed the story?

So What Really Happened?

1. Lord Dufferin was a lively and popular person. After dinner parties he would entertain friends with stories. When the candles burned low and the night winds howled, what better than a ghost story to thrill his listeners?

2. One of Lord Dufferin's favourite ghost stories was about a woman who answered the door, only to find a hearse waiting outside. The ugly undertaker asked if the woman was ready to go with him. She refused . . . as you would . . . and slammed the door. The ugly man turned up many years later as a lift attendant. Remembering the old vision, the woman refused the lift – it crashed and she was saved.

3. Every time Lord Dufferin told this story he changed it a little. One evening, to entertain a bored nephew, he told the story as if it had happened to him! But the young nephew believed every word and in years to come repeated the story and said that he knew for a fact it had happened to Lord Dufferin.

4. So the spooky story became a fact in the eyes of many listeners. Twenty years later it was published in a book, and proved to be full of factual mistakes. Why didn't the writer change the story when he discovered this? Because it made a better story the way it was told – and good ghost stories make money. Other writers

copied the story and, of course, swore that it must be true simply because they had read it. When some people hear a good story, they like to believe it. But when that same story is put in a book, then nearly everyone believes it!

5. If you are looking for the truth about ghosts, then the message is simple: *don't* believe everything you read!

FIVE EXPLANATIONS FOR GHOSTS

1. **Spirits of the Dead** – Every human has a body (flesh and blood and bones and so on) and a spirit. The body will wear out eventually but the spirit can live on without the body. It may then return to relive its life or to tell its story to any living person who cares to listen.

2. **Energy Recordings** – When something dramatic or violent occurs with humans, a lot of energy is released. This energy leaves an "imprint" in the air – the way people can make an imprint on video-tapes. This "recording" can then "replay" itself and the characters in the violent event can be seen time and again in the same place.

3. **Imagination** – Human beings have a very powerful imagination and can't always control it. If you are in a dark and lonely place then you might be terrified of seeing a ghost. This makes your brain "create" a ghost in front of your eyes. It seems real at the time – but then so does a dream when you are asleep. Ghosts may be waking dreams.

4. **Fraud** – People lie about seeing ghosts – it makes a good story to impress friends. Some people enjoy scaring others with conjuring-type tricks that create the sounds and images of ghosts. And some can make a lot of money out of lying and cheating with ghosts.

5. **Space-Time Warps** – Our universe is not solid – it just looks that way to our simple brains. In fact there are many universes all existing side-by-side in the same space. Sometimes the fabric of our universe cracks for a moment and we see into another time and another place. So if someone walks across a field in another universe – in our universe that may be a house. The ghost walks clean through the wall of our house because it isn't there for him. Or maybe it is not a space-warp but a time-warp. The past, the present and the future are all happening at the same time. Sometimes we move "sideways" in time instead of forwards and see something happen in the past or the future.

T·H·E
VaNISHING
VILLAGE

People have been fascinated by life in other parts of the universe ever since humans first looked up and saw the stars. Sometimes alien life seems the only explanation for the strange and horrific occurrences on our own planet. Occurrences like that in a village in Canada earlier this century . . .

Lake Anjikuni, Canada – Winter 1930

The sky was purple-black and endless. The stars burned cold as splinters of ice. The wind seemed to be even colder. It stung the faces of the two men as they staggered home under the weight of the dead animals they had slung over their backs.

Ice began to form in the beard of the old man, Armand Laurent. His son, Raoul, stumbled behind and cursed the dark that made him trip on the tree roots. A mile to go and the shelter of the cabin. Ten minutes walking and ten more minutes for a fire to thaw his aching eyes.

At first Raoul thought he was seeing things. He thought his eyes were playing tricks as the trail turned blood-orange in front of him. But his father stopped and looked around too. Even his father's frosted beard was sparkling in the light.

Armand was looking over his son's shoulder. Raoul had never seen his father show fear. The old man's eyes were wide and glittering with terror now.

Raoul dropped the frozen carcasses on the snow-covered path and turned stiffly. He blinked up into the sky. The stars had vanished. Another light, much brighter, had swallowed them – a brilliant bar of light as bright as a glowing-hot poker.

The light hung in the sky about twenty miles to the north. Slowly at first, then faster, it began to move. It began to move towards the trappers. Raoul snatched at the dead animals and stumbled down the trail. His father tumbled after him.

They didn't stop until they reached the safety of the log

cabin. But by that time the light had shrunk to a star-sized dot, then vanished. Armand slammed the door and bolted it fast, as if the bolt could keep the terror out.

Next morning they rose and ate. Then they skinned the trapped animals. They went about their lives like two men walking in their sleep. They didn't speak about what they had seen.

Three days later their silent work was disturbed by a knocking at the door.

The man seemed to be knocking on the door of the wooden cabin with something metal. "Mr Laurent! Royal Canadian Mounted Police here! Could I see you, sir?"

Armand pulled back the bolts, lifted the latch and squinted out of the gloomy cabin into the snow-bright evening light.

"Good evening, Mr Laurent," the young Mountie said. His face was red with the frosted air, and ice was dusting his black hat and overcoat. He stamped his feet on the frozen ground and tried to smile a stiff grin. His weary horse blew clouds of steam into the still air.

"Er . . . evening," Armand nodded. His sharp blue eyes looked down at the metal object in the Mountie's hand. It was a gun. He started back.

The Mountie looked down and laughed. "Just used it as a door knocker. You don't seem to have one!"

"Don't need one," Armand replied gruffly. "Don't get many visitors when you're twenty miles from the nearest town."

The Mountie nodded and looked past the old man into the warm darkness of the cabin. "I was just wondering if you could help me," he said.

"Help you with your enquiries? Is that it?" Armand asked sharply. "Look, mister, I'm just a poor trapper, catching and skinning animals for a living. I haven't broken any laws!"

The Mountie shook his head wearily. "No, no, Mr Laurent.

Nothing like that. I'm just not too sure of the trail ahead and I thought you might be able to help me. They reckon you know every inch of trail for a hundred miles around, sir."

"Yep," Armand nodded and couldn't help relaxing a little. "Where are you headed?"

"Lake Anjikuni, sir."

"An Eskimo village? You're half a day's ride from there. You'll never make it before nightfall, son."

The Mountie sighed. "You reckon I could stable my horse here for the night?"

Old Armand looked doubtful. He rubbed his thin grey beard. "I'd pay, of course," the Mountie said.

Armand's face lightened. "Raoul!" he called over his shoulder. "Take this gentleman's horse and put it in the barn. Give it oats, hay and fresh water!"

Raoul hurried to obey his father as the old man led the way into the log cabin and the warmth of the stove. With the horse stabled and a good meal inside him the young mounted policeman seemed keen to talk to the Laurents. "Duvall's my name. Sergeant Alain Duvall."

"And what brings you out here?" Raoul asked. "We don't see many Mounties round these parts."

"We had a report from a trapper in this area – guy called Joe Labelle. You know him?"

"Of course. We sometimes work together," Armand said.

"Seems Joe Labelle came into town yesterday with some crazy story about people going missing from the Eskimo village by Lake Anjikuni. I was sent out to investigate. Took me longer to get here than I reckoned. You'll know Lake Anjikuni, Mr Armand?"

"Sure. The Eskimo hunt and trap and trade just like me."

"And you don't know anything about missing people?" the Mountie asked.

"No-o," the trapper said uneasily.

"They probably went out to see the lights," Raoul said quickly. It was the first time the young man had admitted he'd seen anything.

His father tried to give him a warning glance. It was too late. "Lights?" the Mountie asked.

"Lights in the sky," Raoul explained. "Didn't Joe Labelle tell you about them?"

The old trapper sighed. "You'll probably think we're crazy. It happens, you know. Men out here, alone, start to see things."

The Mountie leaned forward and the red light of the stove gleamed in his eager eyes. "Just tell me what you saw, Mr Laurent."

"It was about three days ago . . . or three nights rather. We'd just emptied the last traps on the ridge and were coming in for supper. We were in the trees on the slope when we saw an orange glow."

"We thought the cabin was on fire," Raoul cut in. "Nothing else round here to make a light like that."

"But we could see it was a light in the sky. It was huge! Never seen anything like it before," Armand said. "Hope I never see anything like it again!"

"What shape was this thing?" Sergeant Duvall asked.

"Cigar," Raoul said.

"Cylinder," Armand said at the same moment.

The father and son looked at each other, annoyed. "To tell the truth it changed as it moved," Raoul said.

"So this bright light was moving? Which direction?" the Mountie asked.

"Across the sky to the north," the trapper said.

"North? Isn't that the direction of Lake Anjikuni?"

"That's right," Armand nodded.

The Mountie rose to his feet and stretched. "If you guide me to the village tomorrow I'll make sure the Mounted Police pay you double," he said. "Mind if I just take this bed over here?"

"Fine!" Armand said and found some blankets for his guest.

The next morning was dull and a freezing wind came down from the north. The three men had to ride into it. After two weary hours they crested the ridge that overlooked the slate-grey lake and the huddle of wooden houses.

The old trapper's sharp eyes narrowed and he squinted through his red-rimmed eyes. "I've never seen anything like that before," he breathed.

"Something wrong, Mr Laurent?" the Mountie asked.

Armand could only shake his head with wonder for the first few minutes. "Nothing there!"

The Mountie gave an uncomfortable laugh. "There's the village there."

"But it's deserted," Armand said.

"We're over a mile away, Mr Laurent. How can you tell?"

The old man gave a bad-tempered wave of his hand. "Not one whiff of smoke from any of those chimneys. And the wind's coming from that direction. We'd hear them from here! The sled dogs are always barking."

The Mountie shrugged. "I know Joe Labelle said there were people missing. I didn't know he meant everyone had gone!"

"They can't have," Raoul said. "There's over twelve hundred people live in that village."

"Let's look," Armand said shortly and led the way down the slippery trail into the village. Ten minutes later they reached the first house.

The Mountie jumped off his horse and hammered on the first door. There was no answer. "Must be out on some hunting trip," he suggested.

Armand Laurent shook his head. "There's a rifle leaning in the doorway . . . no Eskimo would ever leave the village without it. Even if he wasn't hunting he might meet some bears on the trail."

The Mountie put his shoulder to the door and pushed. The weak lock splintered. The house was as cold inside as it was out. A leather coat lay on a bed. It was half-mended. Two bone needles lay beside it. "They must have left in a hurry," he said.

Raoul was exploring the second room. "A pot of stew in here. Caribou by the look of it!"

"I could use a bite," his father said.

"Not of this stew. It's been cold for days." Raoul put a hand to the ashes of the fireplace and shook his head. "No fire here for three days at least."

"Three days?" the Mountie said, coming through the doorway behind him. "Three days since you saw those lights, wasn't it Mr Laurent?"

Armand just nodded. "They left in a hurry. Didn't bother eating before they went . . . and they didn't take the over-land trail or they'd have taken their rifles."

"Maybe they got scared by the lights and crossed the lake," the Mountie suggested.

The three men left the house and crunched down the deserted, snow-covered street. No human tracks broke the crisp white mantle of fresh snow. They turned towards the lake edge and stopped before they even reached the small wooden landing stages. Boats and kayaks crowded the mooring posts. "Must be very near every boat in the village there," Armand said. "Twelve hundred people didn't leave across the lake."

Sergeant Duvall looked up at the snow-filled clouds. "We got time to check the trail out of the village?" he asked.

"This way," Armand said. He led the way through the village. There was no sound, no movement, no warmth in a place that had been overflowing with life just a week before.

They found the dog sleds first. They had been tied to the trees on the edge of the town. Then they had been abandoned. The dogs had died of the cold and hunger. The Mountie was sickened by the sight. "I'd better get back and report this," he said. "If we leave now I could get back to base before night."

But Armand was looking back at the village. One field on the edge was not lying smoothly under the snow. It was pitted with deep trenches that were only half-filled by the drifts. He walked towards it silently, leading his horse. When Sergeant Duvall reached his side he was standing staring at the field.

"What is it, Mr Laurent?"

Armand pointed at the empty troughs. "It's not just the living that have gone from the village," he croaked. "This here was the graveyard. And it looks like every single grave has been emptied!"

He looked up at the grey sky as small needles of stinging snow fell silently from it. "Just what in hell's name was that light?" he asked.

The Royal Canadian Mounted Police searched with every available man and found nothing. They searched for years and never found a clue to the mysterious disappearance of twelve hundred people. People who believe in alien unidentified flying objects (UFOs) think there is a link with the lights seen in the sky at the same time. No one else has been able to come up with a more sensible explanation.

Unidentified Flying Fears – FACT FILE

1. Unidentified flying objects (UFOs) have been blamed for many mysterious disappearances including . . .
– ships and aircraft that have vanished in the so-called Bermuda Triangle
– Missing satellites that have been lost while orbiting the earth.

2. UFOs have also been used to explain mysterious appearances such as . . .
– the Loch Ness Monster
– the Pyramids of Egypt – built by humans under the guidance of alien Pharaohs
– Jesus – who was a flying-saucer pilot from Saturn.

3. Ninety per cent of UFOs are explained as natural or human happenings. People have usually seen . . .the planet Venus, aircraft, comets, meteors, giant balloons, cloud formations, ball lightning, army or shipping flares, or even flocks of migrating geese.

4. UFO experts (Ufologists) have different ideas about where aliens might come from. They say they come from . . .
– Mars – the number of UFO sightings is very high when Mars is at its closest point to earth

– the Milky Way – though *we* know nothing which travels fast enough to reach us from there . . . perhaps aliens do
– the earth itself – aliens reached us years ago and live in colonies on earth (the South Pole being a popular idea)
– inside the earth – with the entrance over the North Pole.

5. Ufologists cannot agree on what the aliens want with us. They say the aliens . . .
– see earth as a sort of entertaining "zoo" of strange human animals
– want to examine us to see what makes us work (and there are hundreds of stories where aliens are supposed to have kidnapped, examined and released victims)
– want to take over earth because their own planet is dying
– do *not* want to take over the earth, but want to keep an eye on us because they are worried about what humans will do if or when they finally develop space travel
– want to make friends and share their knowledge with us.

6. Reports of strange sightings go back to the thirteenth century when monks at St Albans sighted "a ship, large, elegantly shaped and well-equipped and of a marvellous colour", while monks in Yorkshire saw "a

large round silver disc" flying over their heads. Glowing discs covered the sky of Switzerland in 1566, while a whole stream of saucers flew over Embrun in France in 1820.

7. Strange marks began to appear in cornfields in Britain in the 1980s – huge circles and patterns that some people believed could only be made by alien visitors. Other people have shown how the circles could easily be faked, but the Ufologists refused to believe them! An even more weird theory is that the circles were made by hedgehogs trampling the corn! Then someone worked out it would take 40,000 hedgehogs charging round together to make even one small crop circle!

8. It's believed that a flying saucer crashed in New Mexico, USA, in 1947. The army discovered it and described a "flying disc". But the next day they changed their story. They said it was simply a crashed weather balloon. Ufologists think the army is trying to hide the truth so that people won't be frightened. William Moore, an American, has been working since 1977 trying to prove that an alien craft really did crash and that the army is lying.

9. There is a vast and unexplored area of the earth where thousands of alien spacecraft could hide . . . the oceans of the world. Two women say they were kidnapped by aliens and examined. The mushroom-shaped spaceships came out of the sea off the coast of Brazil. The aliens looked like huge rats with narrow slits for mouths; they had thin arms and grey, sticky skin. The aliens told the women that they had a base at the South Pole and a tunnel that took them out under the ice.

A
KILLING
IN KILDARE

Ireland is a country famous for its links with the supernatural. In Ireland no evil-doer is safe from the sort of freak bad luck that befell the killer of County Kildare . . .

Kildare, Eire – 1880

The body should have stayed hidden forever. It was buried in a shallow grave beneath the fine green turf.

But this was Ireland.

Patrick Freeley and his son, Sean, left their cottage and crossed the fields and began to push their wooden spades into the turf. Just beneath the surface was the mush of brown and rotten plants – peat. It would dry out and make fine, slow-burning fuel to see them through the winter.

"Father!" Sean cried suddenly. "I broke my spade!"

The old man straightened and rubbed his aching back. "You always were a careless lad, Sean," he sighed.

"No, father. It hit something hard under the turf," the boy argued.

"Probably a log . . . I'll dig it out for you," Patrick offered.

He pushed the spade carefully into the peat and found the solid thing that blocked his way. The old man slid the spade under the thing. He gave a quick twist of his strong wrists and hauled it out of the ground.

"Holy Mother!" Sean croaked and crossed himself quickly.

His father stepped back and the thing fell back into its peat grave. A flabby, white human hand on the end of a long-dead arm. Patrick muttered a quick prayer then set about uncovering the rest of the body.

He removed the covering turf as gently as a nurse might remove a bandage. The clothes were stained dark with the long soaking in their damp, brown tomb – they looked curiously old-fashioned to young Sean, who was just sixteen.

The face appeared like a pale, sad moon. It was fresh as the day it had died. Patrick knelt on the damp earth and brushed away strands of peat from the young features. "Ah, Michael," he murmured. "Praise God, you're dead."

"You know him, Father?" Sean asked.

Patrick rose and his creased face was pinched with pain. "Aye. And his father, poor old Tom Deeley. I wish old Tom had lived long enough to see this."

"To see his son dead?" Sean gasped. "What father in his right mind would want to live to see his son dead?"

"Tom Deeley would," Patrick said. He took a piece of turf and folded it carefully over the face. A sign of respect before he stood and looked over the folds of the hills. "Let's leave this to the police, shall we?"

The two peat-cutters set off down the brown path between the green banks towards the nearest town. "Young Michael Deeley was a wild lad," Patrick began. "Full of fun and mischief . . . but no real wickedness. And he had a dream. A dream that he'd go to America and make his fortune. He was desperate to save enough money to go. But saving money was hard in those days. Times are hard now . . . they were harder then. So, when he disappeared, folk said he'd gone to America."

"But, Father, why did you say that it was good that he was dead?" Sean asked.

"Young Michael had offered to take two bullocks to market for me. He'd done it before and I trusted him. He'd sell them at market and bring me the money. It saved me a journey and I'd give him a little towards his American dream. But that last time he never came back. I went to Tom Deeley's house to see if he'd come home. He hadn't. We waited up till midnight. We thought maybe he'd stopped at the market for a drink or two . . ."

"But he never came home?" Sean said.

"No. Of course old Tom was upset enough at Michael's disappearance. We thought maybe he'd been robbed on the way home. But what really hurt Tom Deeley was when folk started putting around a story that young Michael had gone to America," Patrick explained.

Sean nodded. "He could have sold your bullocks, pocketed the money and gone on the next ship."

"Aye. I never believed it myself, but it hurt old Tom to know people were calling his son a thief," the man said. "And there was nothing he could do to prove otherwise. The shame took him to an early grave. As I said, he'd rather see his son dead than branded a thief. And the village never quite forgot young Michael Deeley. Just last week we were talking about him in the tavern."

"That's strange, father," the boy said.

"You see, it was just twenty-one years last month since Michael disappeared. Now, as you know, you can sign up for twenty-one years' service in an American city and retire on a grand pension. If Michael had gone to America then he'd have been due home about now with that fortune he dreamed of." The man sighed. "At least he can come home to the village churchyard and lie with his father and mother."

The peat-cutters fell silent and marched the seven miles to the nearest town.

Police Sergeant Shannon was not going to walk seven miles to look at a long-dead body. "We'll take the pony and cart!" he announced. So he set off with the Freeleys to the site of the lonely burial.

"Aye!" Sergeant Shannon shouted over the clatter of the wheels. "I wish old Tom had lived to see this!"

"Just what I was telling young Sean," Patrick Freeley agreed.

"Whoa!" the policeman cried and hauled on the reins of the patiently plodding pony. A stranger was standing by the side of the narrow road to let the cart pass. But Police Sergeant Shannon was the sort of man who liked to know everyone's business. "Good afternoon!" he called. "Would you be heading our way, sir, and could we offer you a lift?"

The stranger smiled. "Mighty kind of you," he grinned and climbed onto the cart.

"American, are you?" the curious sergeant asked.

"No, I just spent twenty-one years there and I guess I picked up the accent," the man said. "I'm a native of County Kildare."

Sergeant Shannon noticed the man's fine cloth suit and embroidered waistcoat. "You must have had a good job in America!"

The stranger stuck out his heavy jaw and said proudly, "Twenty-one years with the Boston police force. Rose to the rank of lieutenant."

"It's a policeman you are, is it!" Sergeant Shannon said, delighted. For the rest of the journey he told the stranger of his own great deeds in the Kildare police service.

It was an hour later when Patrick Freeley called, "Stop here, Sergeant Shannon!" and the policeman pulled the cart to a halt.

"Why are we stopping?" the stranger asked.

"Ah, it's a case you might be interested in yourself!" he cried. "You being a famous Boston policeman may be able to help me solve the mystery of the man in the peat!"

"What man?"

"Come along and see," the sergeant urged.

Slowly, reluctantly, the stranger followed the three men to the shallow grave beneath the turf. He stayed silent while the Irish policeman peeled back the turf that covered the face of Michael Deeley. Sergeant Shannon placed a hand beneath the dead man's head to lift it clear of the grave. "The skull's been crushed at the back here! I think that makes it murder, don't you?" he asked.

The stranger had turned as pale as the dead man. "It should be a skeleton," he whispered in horror. "It should be rotted beyond recognition years ago!" His jaw hung loosely open and his eyes reflected the purple hills like pools of solid glass.

The sergeant nodded, " 'Tis the minerals in the peat, they say. Preserves a body like one of those mummies. But this is the body of Michael Deeley all right!"

Then something strange and horrifying happened. As the sergeant lifted the head further forward, the body folded at the waist and a jet of water gushed from the mouth.

The water stained the fine brown boots of the stranger and he gave a choking cry, "No, Michael! Michael, forgive me!"

Sergeant Shannon asked, "You know this man, then?"

The stranger's eyes were fixed on the corpse and he spoke quickly, his Irish accent returning stronger than ever. "He looks just the way he did the day I killed him. He was so proud of the money he'd made at the market. Ten pounds for those two bullocks. Ten pounds. And all I needed for my passage to America was those ten pounds. And I followed him. Followed him as he made his way back home in the dark. I hit him with a branch – I didn't mean to kill him!"

"But you did," Sergeant Shannon said and his voice was cold as Michael Deeley's grave.

"But I did. I buried him here . . . I went to America. I wrote home from time to time. They never said they found the body! I thought I was safe! Safe!"

"You'll hang for this murder," Sergeant Shannon said.

The stranger nodded. "Michael's just been waiting for this moment, haven't you, Michael?" the stranger whispered.

"Michael could wait," Patrick Feeley said bitterly. "The shame is his poor old father, Tom, couldn't."

Sergeant Shannon took the stranger roughly by the arm. "You're right, Patrick. I wish old Tom Freeley had lived long enough to see this!"

The stranger was too shaken to ever deny the murder. "Justice" had waited twenty-one years to catch him. He pleaded guilty and died on the end of a hangman's rope.

Irish Horror – FACT FILE

1. Irish legends are famous for their "fairy people" – but their "fairies" aren't cute little ladies with wings and magic wands. They're almost human in size, sometimes taller, and not always kindly towards humans. They can lure you to their country with their haunting music and make you their slave.

2. One Irish story tells of a man whose wife was kidnapped by the fairy people. He could only rescue her by throwing a jug of fresh milk over her as she rode past on Hallowe'en. Unfortunately the milk had two drops of water in it so the spell didn't work. His wife fell from her horse, the fairy people gathered round her. She disappeared . . . but left a ghastly trail of blood on the road. This was the revenge of the fairy people.

3. Irish graveyards can also be dangerous. A young man went to the funeral of his girlfriend. As he stood alone by her grave a young woman came and spoke to him. She made him promise to meet her there in three weeks' time. She then asked him to seal the agreement with a kiss. As he gave her the kiss her head turned into a skull. This hideous vision drove him mad. Within three weeks he was dead. He was carried to his grave . . . and he carried out his promise to meet the young woman again in the graveyard.

4. The Irish word for "fairy woman" is "banshee", but banshee has come to mean something else. It is the phantom that haunts the members of one particular family. When someone in the family is about to die, the banshee appears and gives a horrible wail. A death is sure to follow.

5. A belief in fairy people has led to at least one horrific death in Ireland. Michael Cleary believed that his wife had been kidnapped by the fairies. The woman he was living with was, he thought, not his wife but a fairy who had been sent to take her place. He tortured his poor wife by roasting her over an open fire. He had the help of eight members of her family. Michael Cleary swore that it could not have been his wife they

killed . . . the dead woman was two inches taller than his wife so she had to be a witch-fairy. He was sentenced to twenty years' hard labour while the others went to prison. Irish children still sing the street song:

"Are you a witch? Are you a fairy?
Or are you the wife of Michael Cleary?"

THE
MUMMY'S
CURSE

Some of the greatest events in history seem cursed before they have even begun. And sometimes that curse has been waiting 3,000 years to happen!

Egypt – 1890

The mummy of Princess Amen-Ra should have been left to rest in peace. She was evil enough in life . . . she was worse after death. She gave the orders that led to more than a hundred men being sold as slaves or cruelly executed. Then Princess Amen-Ra was stabbed by one of her lovers. She died fifteen hundred years before the birth of Christ. As was the custom, her body was preserved as a mummy.

It was dried in salts and wrapped in bandages. And magical charms and spells were written on reed-paper and wrapped inside the bandages. Some say the charms were to scare off evil spirits. Others say the charms were a curse that would bring doom to whoever disturbed the princess's rest.

Her charmed body was placed in a stone coffin and hidden in a deep rock-tomb on the banks of the Nile. The Pyramids' tombs had all been robbed. The rock-tombs seemed safer from the grim and greedy grave-robbers. But eventually they found her.

They robbed her tomb of all the gold and treasures that lay beside her. Then the robbers were left with just her mummy in its coffin. Worthless to the thieves . . . unless they could find someone willing to buy the three-thousand-year-old lady. They were in luck. Mummies had become fashionable in Victorian Britain. People bought mummified hands and feet as decorations for their homes!

Now four young men arrived at Luxor, keen to take souvenirs home. The thieves must have rubbed their hands in greedy glee. The four young men drew lots. The winner got to buy and keep the mummy in her fine stone coffin.

The winner paid the thieves in cash; it cost him several hundred pounds. He had the coffin taken to the hotel where he was staying. That was when the curse began to waken from its ancient sleep and work upon the men. The first young man, the one who bought the mummy, said, "I'm going for a walk!"

He walked towards the desert. He was never seen again.

Next day the second man began to argue with his Egyptian servant. The servant drew a gun and shot the young man in the arm. The wound began to fester. The surgeon only saved the young man's life by cutting off his arm.

The third young man went home to dreadful news. His whole life's savings were in a bank . . . the bank had failed and all his money had been lost.

The fourth young man fell ill, too ill to work. He lost his job and ended his days selling matches on the streets.

The stone coffin, or sarcophagus, came to England where a businessman in London bought old Amen-Ra.

He gave it to the British Museum – it seems that three of his family were injured in an accident, then his house caught fire not long after the mummy reached his home.

The museum took the gift. The cart arrived in the museum yard. As it was being unloaded the horse took fright and pushed backwards. The cart skidded over the cobbles and crashed into a wall. It trapped a passer-by. He ended up in hospital.

Two workmen carried Amen-Ra into the building. As they climbed the stairs the coffin slipped. The first man fell and broke his leg. The second went home quite healthy . . . then died just two days later.

Surely Princess Amen-Ra should now rest in peace? She couldn't. Watchmen heard her crying in her coffin. Priceless things inside her room were lifted up and dropped. One museum keeper claimed that he had been attacked.

Cleaners would not, of course, go near the withered lady. One man flicked her with a duster just to show that he was not afraid. Within the week his child had died of measles.

So Amen-Ra was locked away and her case was taken to the basement where she'd do no harm.

A newspaper took the story and sent their best photographer. But something happened to the photo – when it was developed it showed a face so fierce and hideous that it scared him half to death. They say he shot himself that night.

The museum sold the mummy and her coffin to another collector. But when a guest said that she'd seen the mummy rise and walk towards her then he had to sell it.

No museum wanted Amen-Ra. No collector had the nerve to take the risk. At last a fearless archaeologist from the United States said he would buy the cursed coffin and the evil Princess Amen-Ra.

It was loaded onto the huge ocean liner and placed in a special compartment behind the bridge on which the captain stood. It was too valuable to be lowered deep into the hold at the bottom of the ship with all the other rich treasures.

She seemed to lie there quietly enough, but . . .

April 1912 – The Atlantic Ocean

On the top deck of the liner the last passengers yawned and stretched and thought about going to their cabins for the night. Mrs Ida Straus turned to her husband. "One more walk along the deck, Isidor, before we go down to our cabin?" she suggested.

He looked over his gold-rimmed glasses. "It's very cold out there," he said.

"But very beautiful," she urged. "Come along. The fresh air will do you good!"

He sighed. It was never any use arguing with Ida when she'd made her mind up about something. He helped his wife into her coat and they stepped onto the deck.

The sea was darker than Isidor's rich black boots, and perfectly calm. The sky was moonless but blazing with bright stars. The liner trembled slightly as the powerful motors pushed it across the Atlantic and the only sound was the band playing somewhere below in the ballroom.

At first Ida thought the deck was deserted. Then she saw the glow of a cigar. A man was standing at the far rail. "Good evening! Lovely evening!" Mrs Straus called.

The man turned and nodded. He held out a hand to Isidor. "Good evening, sir. I'm William Stead."

"Ah, the writer!" Isidor said, shaking the hand of the man with the thick grey beard. "This is my wife, Ida, and I am Isidor Straus."

"Mmm, the congressman and banker," Stead nodded.

"I like your stories, Mr Stead. Good adventures. A good read!" Isidor said eagerly.

"Ooh!" his wife shivered. "Too gruesome for me!"

Stead looked surprised. "Gruesome, Mrs Straus? Which of my stories could you consider gruesome?"

"The ones about talking to spirits of the dead," she said firmly.

"You don't believe in such things?" the writer asked.

"I do. That's why they scare me!" she smiled but didn't look too scared. "Is that what you're doing out here? Talking to the spirits of the Atlantic?"

Stead laughed. "No . . ."

"Spirits of this ship, then? Surely it's too new to have ghosts of old dead sailors on board!" Ida chuckled. The banker sensed that there was something Stead was holding back. "But?"

"It's nothing."

"Come on, man! What do you know about this ship that's so secret?" Isidor urged.

Stead shrugged. "A feeling. Something uncomfortable. Something I sense every time I go near the bridge of the ship."

"No need to worry, Mr Stead," Ida said and patted his arm. "Someone told me yesterday that God himself couldn't sink this ship."

"Stead won't believe that, my dear!" Isidor laughed. "I seem to remember he once wrote a story about a disaster at sea. An unsinkable ship that sank! Isn't that right, Mr Stead?"

"That was twenty years ago," he said.

"Don't worry," Isidor said to his wife. "If the spirits had told him that this ship would sink then he wouldn't be here now, would you, Mr Stead?"

The banker blinked. "Mr Stead? Mr Stead!"

"Oh . . . sorry, Mr Straus . . ." the writer stammered.

"What are you looking at?" Isidor demanded.

"A patch on the stars – look to the right. The stars are filling the sky . . . but over there . . . follow my arm . . . see! Something huge blotting them out!"

"Good lord!" Ida exclaimed. "What on earth can it be?"

Stead licked his lips which were strangely dry. "It's monstrous! Some sort of shadow across the stars! It's getting bigger every second!"

"No!" Isidor said firmly. "It's just that we're getting closer."

Suddenly a faint voice cut the crystal air. "Iceberg dead ahead!"

"Ahh!" Ida Straus sighed. "Just an iceberg! You were beginning to frighten me there, Mr Stead, with your stories of sinking ships and shadows swallowing the ship."

Stead gave a weak smile. "Sorry, Mrs Straus. Yes, we can see it now. Now that the lights of the ship are catching it. Just a huge block of ice!"

"Huge indeed!" Isidor gasped. "Why, it's higher than the mast . . . and so far south, who'd believe it?"

"Ah, the ship's turning now. We're going to miss it," Ida murmured.

As she spoke, the ship swung slightly and brushed against the mountain of ice. The deck beneath their feet shuddered as it scraped against the much larger mountain below the waterline. The iceberg passed out of sight behind them.

"So, your horrors of something fearful lurking on this ship were wrong, Mr Stead. Come inside and we'll have one last drink. I think the bars are still open," Ida smiled and led the way into the warm saloon.

Stead followed slowly. He still felt uneasy. The ship had drifted to a halt. Somewhere below there was the sound of clattering feet and anxious voices.

Ida Straus took his arm gently. "You worry too much, Mr Stead. Everyone knows the *Titanic* cannot sink!"

Five *Titanic* Truths – FACT FILE

1. Isidor Straus and his wife died when the *Titanic* sank. Women and children were offered the places in the lifeboats first – she refused to go without her husband, saying, "We started together and, if need be, we'll finish together." They made sure that their maid was safe then went, arm in arm, back to their cabin to wait to die. Like many others that April night, they died so that others would have the chance to live.

2. William Stead wrote his story of the liner disaster in 1892. It was remarkably like the real disaster of the *Titanic* twenty years later – but it didn't stop him making the trip. He was last seen reading alone in one of the smoking rooms. A crewman, passing the room, said he looked as if he planned to stay there whatever happened. Stead was never seen again.

3. Stead's story was an amazing prediction. But a writer called Morgan Robertson came up with an even stranger tale. His story, *Futility*, told of a liner that was the largest and finest ever built – just like the *Titanic*.
– On its maiden voyage across the Atlantic it hit an iceberg and sank – just like the *Titanic*.
– It lost more passengers than it need have because it carried too few lifeboats – just like the *Titanic*.
– Robertson's ship was 800 feet long; the *Titanic* was 882.
– Robertson's ship had three propellers; so had the *Titanic*.
– Robertson's ship hit the iceberg at 25 knots; the *Titanic*, 23.
– Robertson's ship had twenty-four lifeboats; *Titanic*, twenty.
– Robertson's ship sank in April; so did the *Titanic*.
Robertson wrote his story in 1898, ten years before the *Titanic* was even dreamed of. So the most amazing "true" fact of all is the name he gave to his ship – the *Titan*!

4. The sinking of the *Titanic* is a particularly famous sea disaster because so many famous people died that night, about fifteen hundred of the two thousand and three hundred people on board lost their lives, and because she was supposed to be unsinkable. But it is nowhere near the "worst" sea disaster for loss of

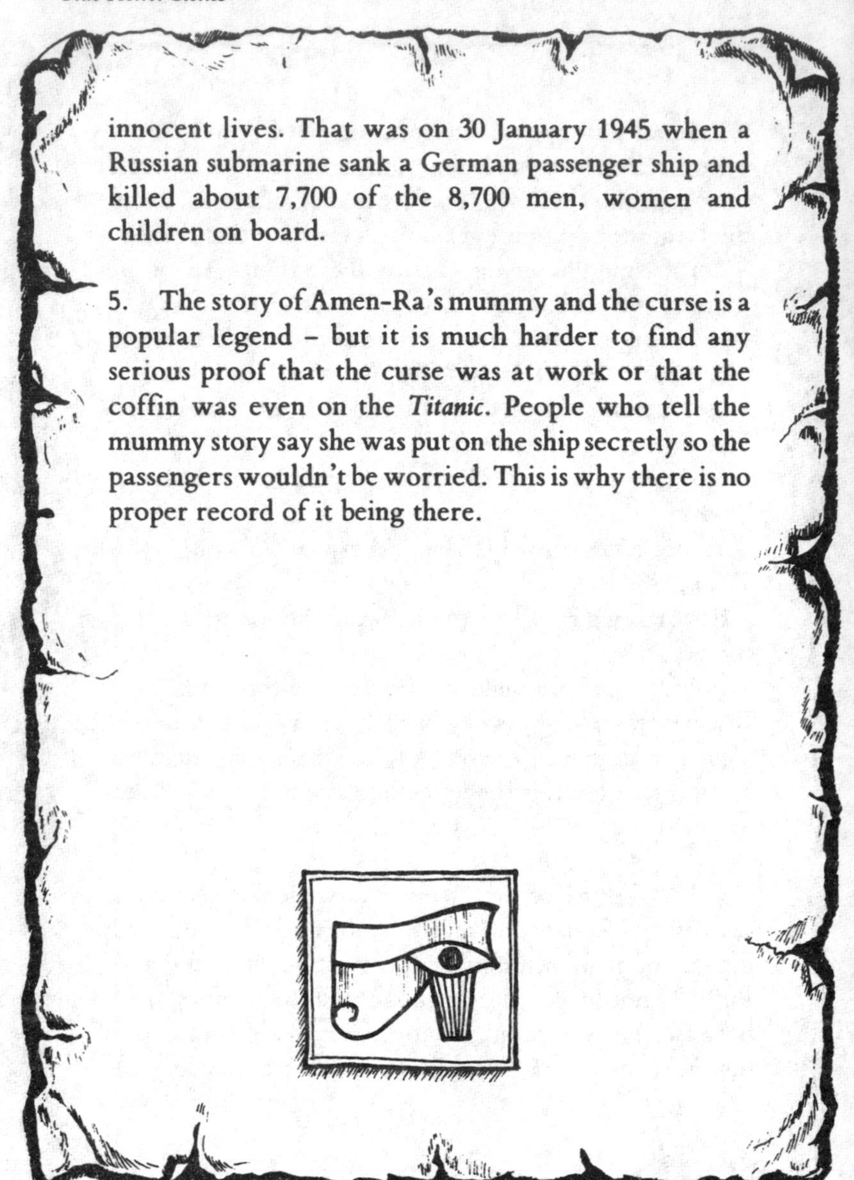

innocent lives. That was on 30 January 1945 when a Russian submarine sank a German passenger ship and killed about 7,700 of the 8,700 men, women and children on board.

5. The story of Amen-Ra's mummy and the curse is a popular legend – but it is much harder to find any serious proof that the curse was at work or that the coffin was even on the *Titanic*. People who tell the mummy story say she was put on the ship secretly so the passengers wouldn't be worried. This is why there is no proper record of it being there.

TRUE GHOST STORIES

INTRODUCTION

Do you believe in ghosts?

Well, do you?

- Is there something outside the natural life . . . a *super*-natural life?
- Do people have spirits as well as bodies?
- Do those spirits survive the deaths of the bodies?
- And if the spirits survive, do they go on to another life? . . . an *after*-life?
- Or do some come back to our world?
- And, if they do come back, can some living people see them?

These are the questions that interest most people. This book will try to answer them honestly by presenting some of the most fascinating cases. The cases are retold as "stories" to entertain you . . . and maybe send some shivers down your spine. But the book then gives some fascinating facts about the stories to help you make up your own mind about the mysteries of the supernatural.

Do *I* believe in ghosts?

Let me tell you my own story. Let me tell you about Mara . . .

Durham, England – November 1993

Mara is a Great Dane dog. When we adopted her she was a poor, thin creature. She'd been badly treated as a puppy and rescued from her cruel owners just in time.

For the first year in our home she was timid and afraid of humans – too timid even to bark. But slowly she learned to trust us. It was a great day when a stranger came to the door and Mara let loose a window-rattling "Woof!"

But she's never really recovered from her bad treatment and her brain is slightly damaged. Sometimes she has a small fit and wakes up shivering and lost. It takes her half an hour to remember where she is.

In the winter of 1993 she was really ill. She raced around wildly and seemed desperate to be out of the house. Someone opened the door and she disappeared along the road.

We waited for her to return. She didn't. Perhaps she had run too far while her mind was disturbed. When she recovered she must have been truly lost.

Snow was lying on the ground that night. Mara hated the cold and loved sleeping in front of the fire whenever she could. A night sleeping out in that February cold could kill her. We reported her disappearance to the police and waited.

The next day there was a phone call. Someone had seen a large, dark grey dog on a farm five kilometres from our house. They told the police. The police told us. My daughter, Sara, and I jumped in the car and hurried to the farm.

It was five o'clock on a bitterly cold evening. The sun had set but the sky was a clear ice-blue and snow lay in a thin, crisp covering at the edge of the road. We turned off the main road and on to the farm track. The farm was two kilometres down the track, but halfway along was a small forest of fir trees that the road cut through.

Let me get the next part right, because it's important.

The farm track ran straight into the wood. I was 300 metres away from the spot where the road entered the wood. As I looked ahead a dog trotted across the road. It was a large, dark dog. I had no doubt that it was Mara.

"There she is!" I cried.

Sara had been looking out of the side window. "Where?" she said.

"She ran across the road and vanished into the wood," I explained.

Sara shrugged. She'd seen nothing. I hurried down the frozen rutted track to the place where I'd seen her and skidded to a halt. There was no dog in sight. But the woods were thick and you could soon have lost sight of an elephant in that undergrowth.

We called her name. Nothing. Then we looked down at the snowy verges. There were the huge paw-prints of our dog.

The tracks seemed to disappear into the wood, but there was a wire fence around the edge and we couldn't follow. After half an hour of following tracks in the snow we climbed back into the car and drove on to the farm. Yes, they'd seen the dog, but that was two or three hours ago. They'd called for her but she'd run away.

We went back to the woods where I'd seen her. It was growing too dark now to see anything. We went home.

As we walked through the front door Mara trotted out to greet us, wagging her tail. At five o'clock she had wandered into the garden of a friend at the far side of the village and been given a lift home, but at ten-past five I'd seen her quite clearly trotting across the road five kilometres away . . . or had I seen her "ghost"?

Could a dog be in two places at once? That's impossible. I *hadn't* seen her. So what *had* I seen?

A "double", a ghost-hunter would tell you. An "apparition".

There are two kinds of apparition – ones inside your head and ones outside. No one else saw Mara at the time I did, so it was probably *all in my mind*. I desperately *wanted* to find her there – as I drove to the farm I could almost picture my first sight of her. I simply saw *what I wanted to see*.

But to this day I would swear I *didn't* imagine it. I'm sure that I saw *something* that looked like our dog. If I didn't imagine it, then I saw a ghostly apparition.

It's an amazing fact that there are more reports of apparitions of the *living* than the *dead*! Some say a disturbed mind (as Mara's is) can throw out images of itself where a sound mind is too much in control.

So, yes, I believe in apparitions. People who have seen a ghost tend to believe in them. People who haven't seen one have to rely on reported stories and decide if they are true. That's what this book will try to help you do.

THE HALLOWE'EN GHOST

The Restless Mummy

Manchester, 1990

"The barn's on fire!" Rory Watson cried, clutching at the wooden five-bar gate.

His sister sighed. She knew it was a mistake to bring Rory out on Hallowe'en, but Mum had insisted, "Take Rory with you, Sarah."

"He gets so excited, Mum. He's embarrassing," Sarah had complained.

"Take him or you don't go," her mother had said firmly. "There are two turnips on the table. Start hollowing them out."

And Sarah had been right. Rory had thrown himself into the trick-or-treat visits as if he really believed he were a ghost. He'd scared the old lady in Osborne Terrace half out of her wits. She'd threatened to call the police.

Now they were on their way home. They had to pass old Birchen Farm. Sarah didn't really believe in ghosts but the place gave her the creeps even in the daytime. Over the years a housing estate had grown up around the farm. Its fields were covered by rows of houses and roads and paths. Now the farmhouse and the barn had only a small paddock with a few grimy sheep.

"It *is*, Sarah! The barn's on *fire*!" Rory insisted.

She sighed again and walked back to where he stood. Sarah peered past the dark house and saw that there was certainly something strange about the wooden barn. Its blackened boards were warped and cracked and through the gaps there was certainly a glow. But that glow wasn't flickering. It was steady. "Someone inside has a light on," the girl told her brother. "Let's go home."

It was as Sarah turned away that she heard the sound. At

first she thought it was an aeroplane taking off from nearby Manchester Airport. It had that whining, hissing tone. She looked up into the sky. Then the sound became more human – a wail of pain or a cry of anger. The girl reached for Rory's arm but he was moving so quickly that she missed. He tumbled past her and sped down the road. Sarah stretched her long legs to catch him. Something banged painfully at her knee. It was the turnip lantern. She threw it in the gutter and sprinted home.

Brother and sister fell through the kitchen door together and it was five minutes before their mother could get the story from them clearly.

She nodded as she sat at the kitchen table. "Yes. There is a story about that farm."

"Tell us, Mum," Sarah said.

Mrs Watson looked at her son doubtfully. Sarah was right. Rory was excitable. "There's a football match on the television, Rory. Why don't you go and watch it with your dad?"

"Okay," the boy said, picking up a can of soft drink and hurrying off to the living room.

"So, what's the story?" Sarah asked.

"Your gran told it to me. She was just a girl when the old mansion, Birchen Bower, was knocked down. She can still remember it. But the story goes back even further. It goes back to the 1740s when a lady called Miss Hannah Beswick lived there. It seems she was a bit of a miser."

"Like Mr Scrooge in the Christmas story," Sarah put in.

"That's right. Miss Beswick was so mean she wouldn't pay someone to manage the farm; she did it all herself until she became too old. They say she made a fortune."

"What did she do with it?"

"In 1745 a Scottish army invaded England. When Miss Beswick heard they were as far south as Manchester she did what a lot of rich people did. She hid her treasures."

Sarah's eyes lit up. "Treasure? What sort of treasure?"

"Mostly silver and gold. She hid it somewhere near Birchen Bower mansion, but she worked alone and no one knew where it was."

"So how do you know it was silver and gold? Did the Scottish soldiers find it?" her daughter asked.

"I'm coming to that," Mrs Watson said. "The Scots never came to Manchester and they were defeated. The war was soon over, but Miss Beswick decided not to disturb her treasure. There were more villains around than Scottish soldiers. She might have lived and died in peace but something shocking happened that changed her life, something so horrible that I wouldn't tell Rory; you know he sometimes has nightmares."

Sarah nodded and looked towards the living room. The door was closed. Her mother lowered her voice. "Miss Beswick's brother, John, fell ill. The doctor went to his house and declared him dead. He was laid in his coffin and Miss Beswick went to pay her last respects."

"What does that mean?" the girl asked.

"She went to have a last look at her brother in his coffin before they buried him."

The girl shuddered and wrapped two hands around her mug of hot chocolate. "That's horrible."

Mrs Watson shrugged. "It shows respect to the dead," she explained. "Anyway, Miss Beswick said goodbye to her brother and the undertaker moved in to put the lid on the coffin and screw it down. But just as she turned away she thought she saw the cheek twitch ever so slightly. She called for a mirror and held it under her brother's nose. It was soon covered with a faint mist. He was breathing!"

"They were going to bury him alive!" Sarah gasped.

"They were. The doctor was called and the 'dead' man was revived. In fact they say he went on to live many more healthy years. But the effect on Miss Beswick was shattering. From then on the old woman had a terror of being buried alive. So she made a curious addition to her will."

"She asked not to be buried for a week or two after she died, I suppose," Sarah said thoughtfully. "That's what I'd do."

Her mother gave a faint smile. "Miss Beswick went one better. She asked to be buried . . . never!"

"That's impossible! She'd go mouldy!" Sarah cried, pulling a disgusted face.

Mrs Watson leaned across the table. "Would she? I thought you were studying the Ancient Egyptians at school this term."

"We are, but . . . but . . . they turned their kings into mummies!"

"Exactly!"

The girl's mouth dropped open. "Miss Beswick asked to be turned into a mummy?"

"Yes. She left money to the family doctor, Doctor White, and to all his descendants on the condition that her body was never placed below the ground. Stranger still, she insisted that her body should be brought back to Birchen Bower once every twenty-one years. And then she died."

"And Doctor White turned her into a mummy?"

"Miss Beswick died so suddenly that her great fortune of hidden treasure wasn't found. But the doctor wrapped the corpse in bandages, leaving only the face exposed, then treated it with tar to preserve it."

"Is this true?" the girl asked suddenly.

"Oh, yes. The body was put on display at Manchester Natural History Museum and lots of people saw it. It was there for over a hundred years. And five times the body was taken back to the old farm. They placed it in the barn."

"In the barn where we saw the light tonight? That's disgusting!" Sarah said.

"In 1868 the museum thought that too. They had Miss Beswick buried in a proper cemetery," her mother explained.

"I thought you said Gran told you this story. Even Gran isn't old enough to remember things from a hundred years ago," Sarah said suddenly.

Mrs Watson grinned. "No, she's not quite that old. But just because Miss Beswick was buried doesn't mean that's an end to the story. You see, she never really left Birchen Bower. The huge mansion was divided into flats. Several families lived there and most of them reported meeting old Miss Beswick's ghost at some time. First there was the rustle of her silk dress, then her figure, dressed in black, glided into the kitchen. She always disappeared at the same flagstone in the floor."

"What was so special about it?" Sarah asked.

Mrs Watson shrugged. "We'll never know. They pulled the old house down. But the barn's still there, and that's where Gran comes into the story. It seems she met a rich man once who told her the story of The Mummy at Birchen Bower. He then said he'd been walking past the barn one Hallowe'en when he saw a glowing light coming from inside. He thought it was on fire, but when he went to investigate the light went out and there was nothing in the barn. He was an inquisitive man, though, and he asked the people in the area what they knew about the old barn. He pieced together the story of Miss Beswick and came up with a curious idea."

Sarah nodded. "The ghost of the old woman was wandering around the barn. But why?"

"That's what the rich man worked out. When would Miss Beswick have wandered around the barn, with a glowing lantern, when she was alive?"

The girl frowned and concentrated. "When . . . when she was hiding her treasure?" Her face cleared. "She hid her treasure in the barn!"

Mrs Watson gave her daughter a playful pat on the head. "Well done, Sherlock! The man went back to the barn and started digging. He found several gold pieces and that's what made him rich. That was back in the 1920s when Gran was just a little girl."

"So why did we see that light again tonight?" Sarah asked.

"Ah, it seems that the theft of the gold just infuriated the ghost. One of Gran's friends was walking past the barn one night and saw the ghost of Miss Beswick again. The old woman was wearing her black dress with a white collar. The figure was making terrible wailing sounds and shaking her fist as if she was upset."

"That would be the wailing I heard!" Sarah said.

"Perhaps, perhaps. Or maybe it was just a jet aircraft from the airport. You don't want to get too scared; you probably just made a mistake."

"But the light?" Sarah said.

"Maybe someone was working in the barn."

The girl nodded and finished her cup of hot chocolate. She stretched. "I think I'll go to bed."

"Sweet dreams," her mother smiled.

"Yes . . . it was just the sound of a jet. And the story's just some old ghost story. It's not as if I *saw* a ghost, is it?" she said.

"That's right," Mrs Watson agreed. "Just don't tell Rory the story. He's not as level-headed as you."

"I won't, Mum. Goodnight."

"Goodnight!"

Sarah was surprised when Rory insisted on walking past Birchen Farm on the way to school the next day.

"You're not scared, then?" the girl asked him carefully.

"Scared? No!" the boy said.

"You ran fast enough last night."

Rory nodded and turned a little red. "You scared me when you started screaming," he said.

"You ran before I yelled," she said.

Rory stopped and frowned. "I did?"

"Yes. As soon as you heard the sound."

Her brother looked at her with wide and wondering eyes. "Sound? I didn't hear a sound."

"The screaming of that jet. It scared me. That's what

must have scared you, dummy!"

"Oh, no," the boy said seriously. "It was that woman that scared me."

It was Sarah's turn to be puzzled. "What woman?"

"The one in the black dress – a long black dress with a white collar. She gave me a real fright!"

"Because you thought she was a ghost?" Sarah asked.

"No! There's no such things as ghosts! It was because she was coming towards us looking very angry and shaking her fist. Maybe she was fed up with kids going trick-or-treating at her door, eh, Sarah?"

"Maybe," the girl said faintly.

"Come on," Rory tugged at her sleeve. "We'll be late for school."

"There are worse things that can happen," Sarah said quietly, looking at the dark and gloomy barn.

"Such as what?"

"Such as being buried alive."

"Hah!" the boy laughed and began to run down the street. "And Mum says *I've* got a strong imagination!"

Ghostly thoughts 1

Apparitions: The image of a dead person is seen as the person was in life.

Explanation? You can *see* images of people long after they have died. You can see them in photographs, films and video recordings. You can *hear* their voices on recordings. Maybe nature has some way of "recording" the most dramatic images of someone's life and "replaying" them at a certain place, at certain times to certain people. Just like a photograph, an apparition can be seen by the living – but of course it cannot see the viewer.

Hallowe'en – FACT FILE

Did you know . . .?

1. Hallowe'en lanterns are a reminder of an old legend concerning an Irishman called Jack. He upset the Devil and the Devil threw a piece of coal from Hell at him. Jack caught it in a hollow turnip and was doomed to wander the earth showing his light till the end of time. Jack-o'-Lantern still makes his appearance at Hallowe'en in the shape of turnip lanterns which are carved out by children.

2. Hallowe'en is known as All Souls' Night – the time of the year when the ghosts of the dead are said to roam about. It is also a time when witches and devils are said to be at their most dangerous and powerful. Imagine that the land of the living and the land of the dead are separated by a curtain. At Hallowe'en that curtain is very thin.

3. Hallowe'en celebrations are an ancient idea. The Celtic people of Ancient Britain held a feast to celebrate the end of summer. The Romans said that the British priests (Druids) made human sacrifices to the gods at the celebration. They claimed the sacri-

fices were made by fastening prisoners in a huge wooden cage and setting fire to it. (The Romans were probably lying.)

4. The Romans celebrated a day of the dead on 21 February but Pope Boniface changed it to All Saints' Day and made it 13 May. A later Pope, Gregory III, changed it again to 1 November. The "eve" of 1 November is, of course, 31 October, and that's when most people celebrate "All Hallows' Eve" (or Hallowe'en) now.

5. On Hallowe'en many children enjoy dressing up and pretending to be ghosts who have slipped through the "curtain" from the

world of the dead. They then call at houses and threaten the owners with a haunting if they aren't given a gift – this is called "trick or treat" in the United States. But a Chinese woman who moved to Britain had never heard of Hallowe'en or the game. She really believed there was a ghost at her door and she threw a pan of boiling water over the eight-year-old boy. Only his mask and bin-liner costume saved him from serious injury. The poor woman was ordered to pay the boy £750 for the scalds he received. Some trick – some treat!

GHOSTS AT WORK
The Phantom Boots

Say the world "ghost" and what do most people think of? A haunted castle or a creepy house? The spirit of a great and famous person? But there's no reason why ghosts should have to live in those draughty miserable places. They can appear in the least likely spots at the most peculiar times.

This story was told by a coal miner, John Kitchin, and he swears it's true . . .

Scotland, 1973

I once knew a night-shift engineer. Sid, his name was. What his second name was I can't quite remember.

He worked up in the main control room of the pit. He uses to dress like that cartoon boy, Dennis the Menace, even though he was fifty years old, and he had this big spiky haircut, straight across the top.

He was in the control room one night, looking after tub-loading, from eleven o'clock at night till seven in the morning.

It's bright up in the control room – better than the filth and dust below the ground. Still, the night shift hours can drag a bit when you're up there all on your own.

Then, in the middle of the night, around three o'clock, he gets a phone call from below the ground; I think it may have come from Number 4 transfer point, somewhere about a mile from the pit-head where two roadways meet underground.

The main conveyor pulls the coal from out the pit. It's the transfer point lad that's on the phone.

Sid says, "What can I do for you, Tony lad?"

"You'll have to stop these belts and get some other feller on my job," the young lad says. "'Cos I'm not moving from this refuge hole!"

The refuge hole is the lad's control box where he watches the coal run down the big conveyor belts.

Sid says, "Well, you know we can't stop the belts. What's the matter with you, Tony lad?"

He says, "There's a pair of boots that's dancing on the belt!"

Now, Sid being Sid, he says, "All right, lad, you've had your little joke. There's no way we can stop that belt."

"You've got to stop the belt and then you've got to get somebody else down here, 'cos I'm not moving from this refuge hole," he says.

So Sid says, "Do you know what that means? What stopping the belt means in terms of lost production?"

He says, "I don't care what it means, 'cos I'm not moving from this hole. And there's a great big pair of boots that's dancing on the belt, I'm telling you."

"Lad," Sid says, "I've been around for fifty years, and I think you've pulled my old leg long enough. There's no way I'm switching off that belt."

Young Tony says, "You'd better stop the belt and then you'd better get somebody down here, 'cos I'm telling you that there's a pair of boots that's dancing on the belt."

The argument goes on for about ten minutes. Finally Sid says, "You just sit down, Tony son, and think about it."

"I've thought about it long enough. I'm staying in this hole until you stop the pair of boots that's dancing on the belt."

Now Sidney thinks, a joke's a joke, but this joke's just gone far enough! The old chap starts to lose his head. "Do you know what you're going to get if you don't stop this stupid game? You're going to get the sack, young man."

The lad says, "I don't care what I get. Just stop the belt and get somebody down there."

Now, if there's a stoppage you have to put the reason, don't you? You have to write that reason in the log book. And Sid hates to write reports. So Sid says, "Right, I've had enough of you. I'm going to call the manager."

"Call who you like," the lad says. "Stop the belt and get somebody down here, 'cos I'm scared."

Sid calls the manager and *he* speaks down on the phone to Tony. "Now then, Tony lad, we'll leave the belt running but we'll send two men down there to have a look. We'll send a man down 'A' shaft and we'll send a man down 'B' shaft. They'll be sure to get these . . . boots."

"That's not good enough! You've got to stop the rotten belt!" the lad sobs.

"We've been in touch with the two deputies. They're coming now, they won't be long," the manager says.

"Are you going to stop the belt?" the lad cries, and he's screaming now.

So the belt is stopped.

That is all the coal work in the mine stopped. The pit can shift six hundred tons of coal in every hour.

The pit goes silent as a graveyard. Time passes as Deputy A and Deputy B walk slowly down the passages to the transfer point. And then, back in Sid's control room, there comes a crackle on the radio.

Deputy A cries, "Right, we've got him! Some bloke climbing on the belt."

A click and Deputy B comes in, "Yes, I can see him. Now we've got him."

Then silence once again. And then a sudden cry. "He's gone!" one of the men cries. "He must have run past you."

"There's no one gone past me," the other says.

"In that case there's just one place he can be. He must have run along that passageway between us."

"Hah!" the first one laughs. "That passageway is blind. There's no way out."

Sid nods to the manager. "They'll catch him now. He's headed down a dead-end passage. Now he's had it. Now we'll see who's playing silly jokes and trying to scare poor Tony there."

"He's for the sack," the manager says sternly.

"What, the lad?"

"No," the manager says. "This bloke that's playing games. He must have cost the pit a thousand pounds already." He taps his fingers on the table top and waits for the radio call. "Come on, come on," he mutters, staring at the radio. "How long is that passage anyway?" he asks.

"It's only short," Sid says. "They must have caught him up by now."

"Then why have they not called us back?"

"Perhaps the feller had a struggle. If they're too busy wrestling with him they can't make a radio call," Sid explains.

It seemed an age before the call came through. Deputy B is almost whispering in the microphone. "There's no one here," he says. His voice is shaking.

"There has to be," old Sid says.

"There's not!" the other deputy cuts in. "It's like he walked into a wall of coal. He never came past me."

"And he never came past me," his mate agrees. "It's dark down here but the passageway is narrow. No one could have run back past us."

"Come back up," the manager says, "and bring young Tony with you."

Half an hour later Tony is sitting in Sid's control room, drinking hot sweet tea.

"I saw the boots!" he says. His face is smudged with coal but that can't hide the grey shade to his skin.

"I might have said that you imagined it . . ." the manager begins.

"But we both saw it too," Deputy A says and he shakes his head. He's worked there longer than old Sid himself. He thought that he'd seen everything there was to see.

"Dancing on the belt," his mate agrees.

"You know the men who work down there," the manager says. "So tell me who it was."

"I couldn't see him very clearly, understand. Just those dusty boots that were dancing on the belt. His head was bent down so it wouldn't touch the roof. I only saw the black cloth cap."

"Cloth cap!" old Sid says. "No one wears cloth caps these days. Not for fifty years or more. They all wear helmets underground."

The man shrugs, "Aye, you're right . . . but this man wore a black cloth cap."

No one cares to argue with the man.

The manager looks down at Tony. The boy has stopped his shaking now but still his pale eyes stare down at the floor. Maybe he's seeing something deep below the ground. "Only the boots," he muttered. "If I'd seen the feller I wouldn't have been so scared. But all I saw were the boots. Dancing. Dancing on the belt like they were happy."

"Maybe his head and shoulders were up in the shadows," the deputy says, quite gentle.

"That's right," his mate agreed. "We saw the whole man . . . both of us."

The lad looks up quite sharp, his eyes as wild as my Uncle Paddy's terrier. "I know what I saw. And I didn't see a man. I saw a pair of boots as clear as I can see you now. I'm not going mad, you know. I'm not, you know. I saw them."

The manager just nods and mutters, "You get off home now, Tony lad. We'll see you back tomorrow night."

The boy stands up, puts the empty cup down and trudges out of the control room.

"There'll have to be a report," Sid says. "We've lost a thousand tons of coal, stopping the conveyor belts like that."

"Yes. Yes," the manager says. "You write up a report."

"Aye, but what do I say?" Sid asks sharply.

The manager turns his collar up and stares out into the early morning dark. "You'll think of something," he says.

"I'll think of *something*," Sid says, angry now. "But can I think of *something* so I won't look *stupid*? I can't go and write those things about a pair of old boots dancing on the belt, can I, sir? Now, can I?"

The manager steps out into the cold and doesn't give an answer.

Then Deputy A rubs a grimy hand over his grey hair. "Young Tony must have had a fright," he says.

"We'll not see that young man again," Sid says.

And Sid was right. The boy went home and never turned up at the pit again.

A few years later old Sid left the pit himself. Only then did he tell the story of the boots – the boots that danced along the belt and cost a thousand tons of coal.

A funny chap, old Sid.

Pair of braces like Dennis the Menace. Big spiky haircut, straight across the top.

Tough as a pit pony, old Sid. But he's still haunted by a pair of boots.

Ghostly thoughts 2

Imagination: Seeing something that isn't really there.

Explanation? Watching a coal conveyor is a lonely and boring job. In the middle of the night, when you're half asleep, it's not surprising if you begin to imagine things. Tony could easily have seen lumps of coal bouncing up and down on the conveyor belt and let his frightened mind turn them into dancing boots.

Charms Against Ghosts – FACT FILE

For thousands of years people have feared ghosts and have made up weird spells and charms to defend against the dead. These include:

1. **Brooms**. People of Eastern Europe believed that putting a broom under your pillow would keep away evil spirits while you slept. English people preferred to lay the broom across the doorstep of the house.

2. **Candles**. The light from a candle was said to keep evil spirits away from the dying. They had to be left burning for a week after the death of the person to protect their spirit. The Irish custom was to circle the dead body with twelve candles.

3. **Cairns**. Piles of stones over a grave are called a cairn. They deter grave robbers and their weight also prevents the dead rising from their graves to haunt the living.

4. **Salt**. Carrying salt in the pocket or scattering it across the doorstep will keep ghosts at bay. Throw a pinch over your left shoulder and it will bring good luck.

5. **Iron**. Iron is a powerful defence against ghosts, witches and other evil spirits. An iron horse-shoe hung on a stable door will protect a house or stable. More gruesome, iron nails taken from a coffin will stop you having nightmares if you drive them into your bedroom door. An iron bar left lying across a grave will stop a ghost rising.

6. **Silver**. Most people know the legend that only silver bullets can kill vampires. This metal is also a defence against ghosts, especially if made into the shape of a cross.

7. **Crosses**. If someone is surprised by a ghost then making the sign of the cross in the air will protect him/her against evil.

8. **Prayers**. Christians believe that saying the Lord's Prayer will protect them against ghosts. They also believe that saying the same prayer ***backwards*** is a way of raising the Devil. A common test for a witch was to ask him or her to say the Lord's Prayer. A witch (a servant of the Devil) would not be able to do it, and would be punished for even one mistake. The accused witch would be very nervous; it would be easy to make a mistake while you were so frightened. So the test was hardly a fair one.

GHOSTLY CURSES
The Flying Dutchman

Some ghosts are said to wander the earth as a punishment for offending a god or a devil. They are cursed, and so are the people they meet. These ghosts don't only appear on land. The most famous sea ghost is probably the Flying Dutchman.

July 1881, Australian coast

George was cold. He paced up and down the deck of the warship to keep warm. He was only sixteen and the youngest sailor aboard *HMS Inconstant*. That was why they gave him the worst job. Being on night watch in the winter seas was uncomfortable . . . and boring.

The ship churned through the icy sea and towards the setting moon. Two or three more hours of darkness, the cadet thought. At least in the daylight he'd be able to see the Australian coast. That would be something to look at, something to break the monotony of deep purple sky and darker sea.

George stared at the ribbon of moonlight shimmering on the sea in front of him. When the ship appeared ahead of him it took a while for him to react. It was so sudden and unexpected. It seemed to have grown from melted moonlight. The wind from the Antarctic stung his eyes as he squinted into it. At the same moment a voice called down from the lookout post at the top of the mast, "Ship ahead!"

It was a sailing ship in full sail, racing over the water. It would cut across the course of *HMS Inconstant* at any moment. The laws of the sea said that the sailing ship had the right of way. George began to run towards the bridge where the First Mate was in control. "Ship ahead, Sir! Off the starboard bow."

"A little late with that sighting, Sir," the First Mate said sourly. "I saw it before you came in."

"Sorry, Sir, it just appeared."

The senior officer gave a brief nod and signalled to the engine room to slow down. He stared through the window at the glowing shape of the sailing ship and frowned.

"It's all wrong. No sailing ship ever sailed that quickly in a light breeze like this. It's all wrong," the officer said. He turned to a sailor alongside him. "Send a signal to that ship. She doesn't seem to have seen us."

"Yes, Sir," the sailor answered and turned on the powerful lamp. He began tapping out an urgent signal but there was no reply from the strange sailing ship.

Other officers of the watch gathered on the bridge to see what would happen next. The sailing ship passed across the bows of *HMS Inconstant* and out of the light of the moon. As it sailed away from the warship it seemed to fade. Within a minute the ocean was as empty and calm as ever. The First Mate took a telescope and scanned the sea. He lowered it at last and shook his head.

"*The Flying Dutchman,*" he said. Some of the older sailors nodded and one or two looked afraid. "Back to your duties," the First Mate snapped and the crew hurried to obey him.

George climbed back to the upper deck and stood next to a midshipman. "What did he mean?" the cadet asked.

"It was a ghost ship, Sir," the midshipman said. "And they do say that anyone who sees her is cursed."

"I've heard about ghost ships, of course. What's the story of this *Flying Dutchman*?"

"Well, Sir, many years ago there was a ship's captain who feared neither God nor his saints. He is said to have been a Dutchman, but I do not know, and it doesn't really matter what town he came from.

"He once set off on a voyage south. All went well until he came near land. He used to boast that no storm, however terrible, could make him turn back.

"On this voyage south he reached the Cape of Good Hope when he ran into a head-wind that would have blown the horns off an ox. Between the wind and the huge waves his ship was in deadly danger. 'Captain,' the crew pleaded, 'we are lost if you don't turn back. We shall sink if you try to go round the Cape in this wind. We are all doomed and there isn't even a priest on board to bless us before we die. We are surely bound for hell!'

"The captain laughed at the fears of his passengers and crew. Instead of listening to them he started singing. The songs were so ungodly that they could have drawn thunderbolts from heaven just by themselves.

"Then the captain called for his pipe and his tankard of

beer. He smoked and drank as happily as if he were in the tavern back home.

"The others pleaded again with him to turn back. The more they pleaded the more stubborn he became.

"The storm snapped the masts and tore the sails away. Captain van der Decken laughed and jeered at the terrified passengers.

"The storm grew more and more violent but the captain ignored it just as he ignored the people on his ship. When the men tried to force him to take shelter in a bay by grabbing the wheel he snatched their leader and threw him overboard.

"As he did this the clouds parted and a shape appeared on the deck in front of him. The shape may have been God himself; if not, it was certainly sent by Him. The crew and the passengers were speechless with terror. The captain went on smoking his pipe. He didn't even take his cap off in the presence of the Almighty.

"The Shape spoke. 'Captain, you are a stubborn man.'

"'And you are a villain! Who wants a nice, smooth voyage? Not I! I want nothing from you, so clear off unless you want me to blow your brains out.'

"The Shape shrugged its shoulders and didn't answer.

"The captain grabbed a pistol, pulled back the hammer and pressed the trigger. But the bullet didn't reach the Shape; it turned around and went through van der Decken's hand. At this his temper exploded and he jumped up to strike the Shape in the face. But as he raised his arm it fell limp and paralysed by his side. He cursed and called the Shape all the evil names under the sun.

"At this the Shape spoke again. 'From this moment on you are cursed. You are sentenced to sail forever without rest, without anchorage, without reaching a port of any kind. You shall never taste beer or tobacco again. Your drink shall be bitter water and your meat shall be red hot iron. Only a cabin boy will remain of all your crew. Horns will grow from his forehead and he will have a tiger's face and skin rougher than a dogfish.'

"Captain van der Decker realized his stupidity and groaned. The Shape went on, 'You will always be on duty and you will never be able to sleep, no matter how much you long for it. The moment you close your eyes a sword will pierce your body. And, since you like tormenting sailors, you shall torment them till the end of time.'

"The captain smiled at the thought. The Shape said to him. 'You shall become the evil spirit of the sea. You will travel all oceans without stopping or resting. Your ship will bring bad luck to all who see it.'

"'I'll drink to that!' the captain laughed.

"'And on the Day of Judgement, the Devil shall claim your soul.'

"'I don't give a fig for the Devil!' he replied.

"The Shape vanished and the captain found himself alone with the cabin boy, who had already been changed into the evil creature that the Shape had described. The rest of the crew had vanished.

"From that day to this the Flying Dutchman has sailed the seven seas and takes pleasure in tricking unlucky sailors. He sets ships on wrong routes, leads them into rocks and wrecks them. He turns their wine sour and all their food to beans.

"The Flying Dutchman can change the appearance of his ship whenever he wants and, through the years, he has collected a new crew. All of them are the worst bullies and

pirates ever to sail the seas. Every one of them is cursed and doomed like the Flying Dutchman himself."

"Thanks," the young cadet said. "It was an interesting story. But you don't believe that stuff about a curse, do you?"

"We'll see, sir," the midshipman said. "We'll see."

HMS Inconstant sailed on over the smooth sea and at daybreak George went down to his cabin. He opened his diary and began to write:

At 4 a.m. the Flying Dutchman *crossed our bows. She gave off a strange phosphorescent light like a phantom ship all aglow; in the middle of the glow her masts, spars and sails stood out in silhouette as she came up on the port bow where an officer of the watch also saw her as did a midshipman who was sent forward. But when he arrived at the bows there was no trace or sign whatever of any ship, near or on the horizon, the night being clear and the sea calm.*

As the cadet finished writing there was a tap on his cabin door. "Breakfast, Your Highness."

Prince George yawned, stretched and rose to his feet. The young sailor later became King George V, but his meeting with the *Flying Dutchman* was an experience that stayed in his memory for the rest of his eventful life.

Ghostly thoughts 3

Demons: Evil spirits that try to interfere with human life. They can take many forms – lights, sounds or voices inside a victim's head, fairies, goblins, phantom animals, or phantom ships like the *Flying Dutchman*. They often enter a human body and possess it; that person then becomes a "witch" and performs evil deeds for the demon.

Explanation? Some religions believe that pure goodness is their "God", but pure evil can also exist in a spirit form as a demon. You may choose to believe that. The superstitious used to say that the only way to get rid of the demon was to destroy the body it lived in – that's why they burned witches. Nowadays we aren't so cruel or stupid.

Sea Ghosts – FACT FILE

The story of the Flying Dutchman *seems very unlikely yet some researchers claim the legend is based on fact.*

The Dutch captain's name was Hendrik van der Decken and he lived in the 1660s. Van der Decken was a greedy and ruthless ship's captain who set sail from Amsterdam to make his fortune in the East Indies. Over the years, countless sailors from around the world have sworn that they've seen something strange on the ocean. Can they all be wrong?

1. **The Dutchman's curse**. Prince George's sighting was backed up by thirteen sailors on his ship and on other ships that were sailing alongside her. If seeing the *Flying Dutchman* was unlucky then the curse worked for Prince George's ship, *HMS Inconstant*. Later that same day the seaman who'd first seen the ghost ship fell to his death from the mast. The admiral of the fleet died shortly afterwards.

2. **The *Lady Lovibond*.** Britain has its own phantom ship. On 13 February 1748 the *Lady Lovibond* was sailing by the dangerous Goodwin Sands off the coast of Kent, England. Her captain, Simon Peel, was on honeymoon, with his bride and several

wedding guests. But a jealous sailor (who was also in love with the bride) killed Peel and steered the ship to disaster on the sands. On 13 February 1798, fifty years later to the day, a fishing boat spotted a ship of the *Lady Lovibond*'s description heading for the sands. The crew heard laughter and women's voices. It sounded as though a party was being held on board. But when the ship hit the sands it broke up and vanished. The same vision was seen in 1848 and 1898. Ghost-hunters were on the lookout in 1948 but saw nothing in the mist. Perhaps in 1998 it will be back . . .

3. **The blazing ghost ship**. America's *Flying Dutchman* is the *Palantine*. It arrived off the coast of Rhode Island packed with Dutch colonists in 1752. A storm drove it off course and washed the captain overboard. The ship was driven on to rocks and started to break up. Local fishermen rowed out and took the passengers to safety but began stripping the ship of its valuable cargo before it sank. To cover up their crime they set the ship ablaze, but as they rowed home they were horrified to see a woman come up on deck. She'd been hiding from the looters. Her screams carried across the water until the flames swallowed her. Over the centuries a blazing ship has been seen by many witnesses off the coast of New England.

4. **The ghost under the sea**. Not only ancient sailing ships are ghostly. The German submarine *UB65* was cursed from the start. Workmen building her had fatal accidents then, on her maiden voyage, an officer was killed in an explosion. From then on the ghost of the officer was seen on board. A new captain and crew were appointed who did not believe in ghosts and for a while the ghost did not appear. But when that captain left the submarine the ghost returned. One sailor went mad with fear and jumped overboard. Still the submarine survived enemy attacks until, near the end of the First World War, it mysteriously blew up, killing the entire crew. An accident? Or a ghost's revenge for his own death?

5. **The "ghost" from the bottom of the sea**. Many "ghost" stories have a sensible explanation. In the late 1890s the schooner *A. Ernest Mills* sank in a storm off the coast of California. A few days later the "ghost" of the schooner appeared, to the horror of the local people. The schooner had been carrying a cargo of salt when she sank. When the salt dissolved the *A. Ernest Mills* bobbed up to the surface of the ocean again. Mystery solved!

6. **The ghostly rescuer**. The first man to sail alone around the world was Joshua Slocum of Nova Scotia in Canada. He set off

in July 1895 but soon met terrible storms in the North Atlantic. After struggling to control his boat for three days Slocum gave up, exhausted. He went below to his cabin to wait for the boat to sink. He couldn't swim. Then, as the storm raged he felt the boat riding smoothly as if a strong hand was at the wheel. When he dragged himself back on deck he saw a man in fifteenth-century clothes steering the vessel. "Who are you?" he managed to ask. "I am the helmsman of the *Pinta*," the man replied. The *Pinta* was one of Christopher Columbus's ships that discovered America in 1492. Slocum found the strength to survive the storm. The fifteenth-century sailor was never seen again.

7. **The leading light**. Christopher Columbus himself had a ghostly experience at sea. When his crew were getting seriously worried about ever seeing land again, he saw a light in the sky. It was a "guiding star" that would lead them to the new world. No one else saw the light and no one believed Columbus. The next day they sighted land; they had reached the American continent.

8. **The avenging ship**. Two Arctic exploration ships, the *George Henry* and the *Rescue*, were heading for the North Pole in 1860 when they met a severe storm. The

crews decided the *Rescue* was about to sink so they abandoned her and sailed off on the *George Henry*. Two months later, as they sailed back to the point where they'd abandoned the *Rescue*, they saw a battered ship following them. It was the *Rescue*. She disappeared into the mist. But that night, as they were at anchor, the *Rescue* came back, heading straight towards the *George Henry*. She seemed to be driving ice blocks towards them – maybe as a revenge for the sailors abandoning her. Finally the derelict ship itself charged towards them. At the last second it seemed to swerve away, as if the ghostly driving force had some pity.

9. **The *Waratah* Disaster**. In July 1909 Claude Sawyer was sailing from Melbourne, Australia to London when he had terrifying dreams of a disaster. He saw himself standing at the rail of his ship, the *Waratah*, when a knight in blood-stained armour rose from the sea and mouthed the word "Waratah!" over and over again. Sawyer was so shaken that he left the ship when it reached Durban in South Africa and decided to take another ship for the second part of his journey. The *Waratah* sailed without him . . . and was never seen again. Or "probably" never seen again. Seventy years after the disappearance, an aircraft pilot reported seeing a passenger ship of the *Waratah*'s description lying on its side in clear water off the South African coast. A search was made but nothing was found. What had the pilot seen?

10. **The *Teazer* Terror**. Another ship haunting the North Atlantic was the *Young Teazer*, an American warship. In 1813 she was surrounded by warships of the British Navy. Lieutenant Johnson did not want to be captured so he blew up the *Young Teazer* . . . and himself along with it. A ship of the *Young Teazer's* description is said to sail menacingly towards ships then swerve away in flames.

THE UNEXPLAINED

The Spirit Stones

Most ghostly happenings have an explanation, natural or supernatural. But sometimes there seems to be no reason why ghostly activity should start . . . or stop.

Upper Blackwood, Australia, 1955

The sun had set but the sky was still a clear blue. The autumn nights were colder now and fuel was expensive, so the sticks that Jean Smith was gathering at the edge of the bush would cook an evening meal – and keep Gilbert and her warm through the night.

The huge farm they worked on was over 300 kilometres from the nearest city of Perth. Strangers hardly ever came this way. That was why Jean was puzzled. She felt there was a stranger nearby, watching her.

She looked around carefully. There was no one in sight. Apart from the scrub bushes there was nowhere for anyone to hide. The blank, dark windows of her wooden cabin stared out at her. They were empty.

She shivered and bent to pick up just a few more handfuls of wood before she went home. And as she bent she heard the whisper of something fly past her neck. A moment later it hit the ground with a heavy thud.

Jean didn't wait to see who was throwing stones at her. She didn't need to. She already knew there was no one there. The woman clutched her precious twigs to her chest and ran for the cottage. At her back she could feel something chasing her. There was no way she was going to turn around and look.

Wood spilled on the porch as she scrabbled at the door handle and tumbled into the cabin. Her husband looked up, wide-eyed, and saw his wife scatter the wood on the floor, slam the door and stand with her back to it. A moment later something heavy crushed into the door and almost splintered the wood.

"Spirits!" Jean hissed. "Evil spirits!"

Gilbert jumped up from his chair and wrapped a comforting arm around her shoulder. "No, Jean. We have done nothing to upset the spirits. It's more likely to be one of the shepherds having a joke."

The woman looked at him doubtfully. "There's no one out there . . . at least, no one human eyes can see."

"My eyes will see him," Gilbert assured her and he moved her gently from the door and opened it.

It was darker now. The fences were black lines against the fading grey of the pastures. The air was still. Nothing moved. In the distance a dingo howled. Somewhere closer another one answered it.

Gilbert squared his shoulders and, keeping his back to the cabin walls, walked around the outside of his home. "Hello!" he called. Only the dingo answered.

Gilbert slipped back through the door and bolted it behind him. He was just about to say something to Jean when he saw something out of the corner of his eye that made him duck. Something white rose from the corner of the room and flew towards his head. It clattered off the wall and fell to the floor. "A golf ball," he said. "One that the kids have been playing with. But how –"

Before he could finish there was a clatter on the tin roof as something heavy landed on it. "Spirits!" Jean moaned.

The man looked at his two dogs sleeping by the cold fireplace. They hadn't moved. "Those dogs know when anyone comes within a hundred yards of here," he said. "You're right, Jean – there's no one out there."

"What can we do?"

"I'll go for help," he said. "You'll be safe enough inside. Bolt the door behind me."

He snatched the keys to his old van and hurried out. As the sound of the engine faded the dogs woke up, jumped to their feet and began barking and howling. The woman slipped the chains from their necks and they threw themselves towards the door. "Get him, boy!" she said and pulled the bolt back. But when the dogs pushed through the opening door they began howling and vanished into the night.

Thud! Something hit the roof again.

Thud! That one hit the wall.

Jean Smith snatched her husband's rifle and pushed the barrel through the opening of the door. But from inside the house an empty jam jar flew across the room and splintered against the doorpost beside her head. She shut the door quickly and sat with her back to it. Every object in the room was a possible enemy now.

It was an hour before Gilbert returned with a neighbour. There had been long spells of silence when Jean had begun to relax, but as soon as she did so she was jerked back into terror by something crashing against the wall.

"Hi, Jenny!" Alf Krakour said as he came through the door. "Gilbert says you've been having a spot of bother, eh?"

Jean nodded dumbly.

"We'll soon get to the bottom of this," he promised and, taking his gun, he walked outside with her husband.

Five minutes later the men returned. Alf had stopped grinning now. "Too dark to see anything," he said. "We'll just bolt ourselves in and wait for them to get tired."

But it was Alf, Jean and Gilbert who were tired by next morning. The bombardment went on all night. When the sun rose the attack stopped.

"What do we do now?" Jean asked wearily.

"Tell the boss," Gilbert said. "Smart man, Mr Roberts. He'll sort it out."

That night Mr Roberts joined them. "Someone having a joke," he said.

"That's what I said," Gilbert put in.

"The attacks stopped in the morning because they knew you would see them throwing stuff," the ranch owner explained. He was going to say more when something hissed past his ear and clattered against the wall. The man's weather-beaten face turned pale. He bent to pick up a stone from the floor then gave a sharp cry. "It's hot!"

"Where did it come from?" Gilbert asked.

"Must have come through the wall," Roberts said.

"But there are no holes in the wall. How did it get

here?" Jean asked. The men had no answer.

"I'll find you a new cabin," the ranch-owner promised.

Gilbert Smith shook his head. "It will make no difference," he said quietly.

He walked to the window and looked out. "There's something out there," he said. "Look."

Hanging in the dark air was an unearthly light. An oval blue light. Suddenly the light moved with an eerie whistling sound and the cabin shook. Jean Smith clamped her hands over her ears but she couldn't shut the sounds out.

Slowly the sounds faded. Jean and Gilbert moved closer together. "We must learn to live with this," she said.

"Then I'll find some specialist help," their employer promised. "There's some sort of Ghost Society over in Perth. I'll contact them. See what they say." Roberts took his hat and looked carefully around the door before stepping out.

The ghost hunters from the Perth Psychic Society tried to explain to the Smiths that this sort of spirit activity was common throughout the world . . . but they couldn't stop it. "It tends to stop by itself," they said.

Jean Smith shook her head slowly. Sleepless nights and fear-filled days had shrunk her. "When? When will it stop?" she asked.

The ghost hunters shrugged. "Who knows?" they said and went away.

The woman bent wearily to gather sticks. It was autumn again. A year had passed since that first stone had been hurled at her. The sun had set but the sky was still a clear blue. The nights were colder now and fuel was expensive, so the sticks she was gathering at the edge of the bush would cook an evening meal – and keep Gilbert and her warm through the night.

She stopped and looked up. There was something wrong, something missing. For the first time in a year she smiled. She knew she *wasn't* being watched. She knew that It had gone away. Whatever *It* was had decided to leave them in peace at last.

Jean clutched the sticks and hurried back to the house. She opened the door. Gilbert looked up from his chair at the side of the fireplace. "I know," he said.

"Why?" Jean asked.

Gilbert stood up and walked across to her. He wrapped a hand around her thin shoulders. "Like the people from Perth said, 'Who knows?'"

Ghostly thoughts 4

Poltergeist: A mischievious spirit that causes a lot of disturbance for a household by throwing objects around and making banging or rapping sounds.

Explanation? Perhaps everyone can move things simply by the power of the mind but most of us do not know how to do it. In some people that power may be released and it goes "wild" for a time. The victim of the poltergeist is actually *causing* the disturbances, but doesn't know it and can't control it.

Haunted Australia – FACT FILE

Many reporters visited the Smiths during their year of disturbances. They found no evidence to back the story. On the other hand, no reporter was willing to spend the night there, and most of the strange things happened at night. As many as 150 stones were said to fall on the roof on some nights.

Most of the world's ghostly experiences have been reported in Europe and particularly in the British Isles. But Australia has its own record of supernatural happenings apart from the Smith case . . .

1. **The Min-Min Light – Western Queensland**

Strange things were seen in the sky in the Smith case but such lights have been reported elsewhere in Australia for hundreds of years. In Western Queensland an oval fluorescent light is seen standing or rolling across the sky. It became known as the Min-Min Light because it has been reported so often in the area of the Min-Min Hotel in Warenda Station. Queensland police have seen it for themselves. On investigation they found the light . . .

- was not caused by camp fires
- was unlikely to have been caused by a mirage effect

• was not car headlights or their reflections. No one has ever been able to explain where the light comes from or goes to, though a farm worker reported seeing the light rising from the Min-Min graveyard around 1917. The worker was riding his horse past the graveyard and, understandably, galloped away from the place when he saw the light. To his horror the light followed him to the edge of the next town, where it mysteriously disappeared.

2. **Lady's ghost – West Australia, 1953**

Lady was William Courtney's greyhound. Every night the dog came to his bedroom and dropped on to the floor where it slept. One night he was half asleep when he heard the familiar sound of the dog flopping to the floor. William Courtney's hand trembled as he reached for the light switch, for that afternoon Lady had been put down by the vet following an illness. When Courtney finally found the nerve to snap on the light, the floor was empty.

3. **Bluebird – Lake Eyre, 1964**

Donald Campbell chose the flat salt-lake in Australia to race his car, *Bluebird*, to a new speed record. During the second run a tyre was damaged and nearly sent Campbell to his death. The support team changed the wheel but were afraid that Donald Campbell

would have lost his nerve after such a frightening experience. When they looked through the canopy he seemed perfectly calm but was staring at the screen. He went ahead with another run and broke the record. His mechanic later asked him what he'd been looking at during the wheel change. Campbell admitted he'd been looking at an image of his dead father that appeared in the screen. The image had said, "Don't worry, my boy, it will be all right." The vision had given him the courage to go on.

4. **The haunted house – Newcastle, New South Wales, 1970**

Michael Cooke thought he had found the perfect house for himself and his wife and baby. But they left in fear after something . . .

- made the baby sit up as if jerked by invisible hands
- rumpled bedclothes on a tidy, made-up bed
- moved toys around
- shook a door knob loudly.

But the final straw came when the ghost put in an appearance. As Michael Cooke described it, "Last night I saw a horrible white face looking out of one of the windows as I walked past. The eyes were white with green in the middle. I was so scared the tears just ran out of my eyes. That was the end. I

was thinking of buying the house but I'll never live there again."

Other tenants had reported similar problems.

THE GHOST'S REVENGE

The Miller of Chester-le-Street

Do some poor souls linger on earth? Are they tied to this world because they have some unfinished business here?

Let me tell you the story of Ann Walker. Then make up your mind.

Durham, England, 1632

The market town of Chester-le-Street stands by the River Wear. A water mill once stood down by the river. James Graham, the miller, lived by the mill in 1632.

The miller worked hard and he worked long hours. It was midnight as he put the last corn in the hopper one chill winter's night, and a damp mist rose from the river.

He came down the creaking wooden stairs and he stopped.

There was someone down there on the flour-dusted floor, yet he knew that the door of the mill had been locked.

"Who's that?" he called, peering down into the gloom. The figure made no reply. He turned up the wick of his lantern and took a step down.

He could make out the shape of a long-haired woman. And as he drew close he could see that her hair was dripping. But where the droplets hit the floor they made no mark in the thin layer of flour.

"Who are you?" he asked and the lantern trembled in his hand.

The woman raised her head. Her pale face was stained with red. It wasn't water running down her hair, but blood. The miller stared and made out four or five deep wounds that scarred her head.

No one could have such wounds and live. "Sweet Jesus,

save me!" begged the miller.

Then the woman raised her bloodied head and looked him in the eyes. "No, do not be afraid," she sighed. "I am the spirit of the murdered young Anne Walker. Sit down, sir, for you look too shocked to stand."

The miller sank down on the lowest step and placed the lantern on the old mill floor. "In God's name, tell me what you want!" he gasped.

"I want revenge," the woman said. "I cannot leave this world while my cruel murderers walk free. I need the help of you, James Graham."

"I'll do my best," the miller said.

"Then listen to my tale," the spirit said. "I lived near here in Chester-le-Street. My uncle, Joseph Walker, is a farmer. Joseph took me to his house. I worked there as his maid. But Joseph took my innocence and . . . I found I was with child."

The miller started to forget his fear. He shook his head in horror at her tale.

"My uncle said I'd have to go away. He said I'd have to leave to hide my shame. He promised I'd be well looked after and then return to keep his house."

"He broke his promise?" Graham asked.

"I left the house about this time of night the last new moon – two weeks ago. He sent his friend to guide me in the dark – a miner called Mark Sharp. Sharp is a tall and fearsome man. Hair black as the coal he digs and shoulders wide as a doorway. I should have been afraid of him, yet I was more afraid of travelling down that moonless road alone. We set off on the road to Durham. My guide did not have much to say. His strides were long and I stumbled as I tried to keep pace with him. I begged him to stop when we had gone five miles, and then he told me that he knew a quicker way. It meant we'd walk across the loneliest part of the moor. But I was tired, so tired, that I agreed. The road was quiet at that time of night. The moor was quieter. Only the sounds of owls and something scuttling through the rough grass. A loose sheep scared me half to death. I asked him how much farther. He told me he could see a light. He pointed to the distant hill. As I leaned forward Mark Sharp stepped behind me. He took his pick and struck me on the head. He gave these wounds that you see on my head."

Her apparition shuddered and the blood dripped to the floor. "The law will not convict those two unless we find your body," Miller Graham said.

She nodded and her hair fell forward. Quietly she told the miller where her body lay. "He threw my body in a coal pit, then he hid the pick axe in a bank nearby. He tried to wash the blood from off his shoes and stockings, but he could not get them clean, so he hid them by the pick."

The ghost began to walk towards James Graham. He scrambled to his feet and backed towards the door. "No one will believe me!" Miller Graham cried.

"But you must *try*. And try *again* until they do!" Anne Walker's ghost protested, "Or I shall haunt you till your dying day and then beyond the grave!"

The man tore at the bolts and stumbled down the moon-washed path. He dared to look behind and saw he was not followed. He hurried home and shivered in his bed.

Next day he went to work. He felt the ghost was just a dream and laughed at his own foolishness.

He did not work so late that night but left the mill

before night fell. After supper he went to bed. The night was peaceful and he sank into a dreamless sleep.

When the moon came up, the spirit of the dead girl rose again. This time she was no gentle, pleading ghost. She was a threatening, fierce ghoul. She tore the sheets from the miller's bed and screamed that she wanted justice.

"Yes, Miss Walker, yes," he groaned. "Give me just one more chance. I will obey." The miller did not dare ignore her threat this time. Next morning he went to the magistrate and told his tale.

"And you say this was not a nightmare, Miller?" asked the magistrate. "And you say you had not been drinking barley wine?"

James Graham looked afraid and pitiful. He shook his head. The magistrate believed the honest man. "We'll do our best," he promised.

A search was made. At Framwellgate a disused pit was found. In the pit lay the body of Anne Walker. There were five wounds in the head. The bloody pick and shoes and stockings lay nearby, as the spirit had said.

The cruel uncle and his friend Mark Sharp were brought to trial. The men denied the charges.

At the trial Walker stood up in the dock and told some cringing lies. Yet, on the farmer's back, the judge could see a shadowy form . . . a phantom of the murdered child.

Farmer Joseph Walker and his evil friend were both found guilty and were hanged for their cruel crime.

So, those of you who say that there are no such things as ghosts, how can you explain Anne Walker's tale?

The body would have lain there still if her spirit had not guided Miller Graham to the spot. The ghost had had her revenge and she could rest in peace. So could Miller Graham.

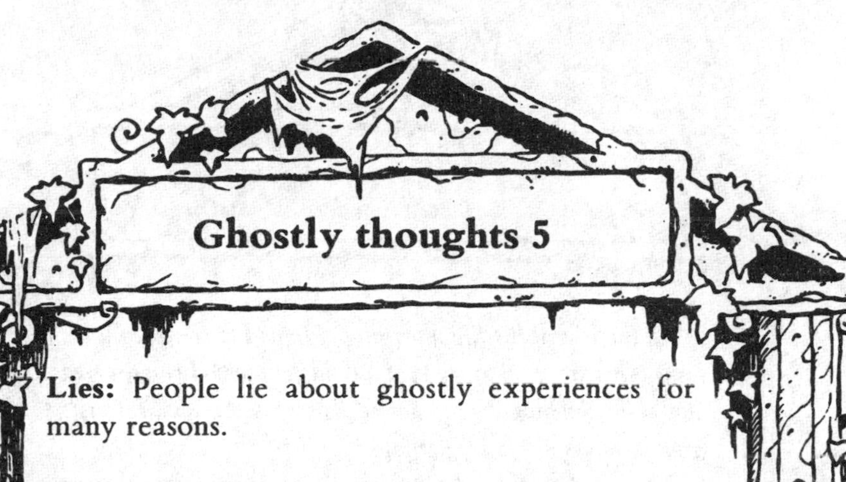

Ghostly thoughts 5

Lies: People lie about ghostly experiences for many reasons.

Explanation? Here is another explanation of the Anne Walker story that does *not* depend on ghosts . . .

Anne Walker lived happily with her uncle, farmer Joseph Walker. She met the local miller, James Graham, when she took corn from the farm to his mill.

James Graham fell in love with Anne Walker. She felt nothing for him. He visited her at the farm. After a quarrel he killed her with the pickaxe that was lying in the barn.

Miller Graham took the body five miles along the road and dropped it down a mine shaft. No one knew about his relationship with Anne Walker, so he was safe.

But he could not sleep at night. He felt guilty about the murder and was terrified of being questioned. Magistrates were looking into her disappearance.

The only way the miller could be safe would be if someone else was tried and hanged for the murder. He couldn't say, "I know where the body is because I put it there," and he couldn't leave the body undiscovered. He'd

spend the rest of his life worrying. He had to come up with some other story. A story that would get the body discovered and point the blame at someone else. A story about a visit from a vengeful ghost, perhaps?

The shadow that the judge saw could be an invention added by story-tellers who repeated it years later.

True ghost story? Or a cunning lie?

Both are possible. You must make up your own mind.

Avenging Ghosts – FACT FILE

The belief that a ghost might wander around this earth until it avenges its death is quite common. Sometimes the ghost appears to a relative, describes its death and reveals the guilty person. In some amazing cases (like the one at Chester-le-Street) no one realized the victim had died until the ghost informed them.

In many cases a ghost seems to have returned to earth for vengeance . . .

1 **The Greenbriar ghost**. Zona Shue died in West Virginia in 1897. Her husband, Edward, was in a terrible state and kept clutching at the body as the doctor was trying to examine it. In the end the doctor gave up and concluded that Zona had died of "an everlasting faint". Even when she was in her coffin Edward would let no one near her. He covered her neck with a scarf ("her favourite scarf!" he sobbed), but Zona's mother took a pillow from the coffin and tried to wash it. She found a red stain that would not come out. Then Zona's ghost appeared to her in a dream. Four nights in a row the ghost told how Edward had lost his temper and broken her neck – the ghost turned her head in a complete circle to show how loose it was! Zona's mother took the

story to the police, they examined the body and found it did indeed have a broken neck, just as the ghost had said. Edward was tried and found guilty. Zona's ghost could rest in peace, knowing justice had been done.

2. **The rapping ghost**. Louise Trafford was killed in 1949 but the police had no clues to the killer. Then a Medium called the detective in charge of the case and said she had evidence . . . from the ghost of the dead woman. The message was in the form of knocking sounds. The police didn't understand the code – it wasn't Morse code – but Louise had spent a term in prison where prisoners would send messages to each other by rapping on pipes. When one of Louise's cell-mates heard a recording of the rappings she told the police exactly what they meant. The message from beyond the grave named the killer and told the police where to find vital clues to convict him. He was arrested, tried and executed three months later.

3. **The Inverawe ghost.** Duncan Campbell was the Lord of Inverawe in Scotland. One night in 1748 he gave a stranger shelter. He didn't know that the stranger had just murdered his cousin, Donald. But Donald's ghost appeared and told the Lord of Inverawe that the murderer was in the house: "Blood has been shed. Do not shield

the murderer." The Lord of Inverawe ignored the ghost's message four times that night. Finally the ghost said, "Farewell – until we meet again at Ticonderoga." Ten years passed. No one had ever heard of Ticonderoga. Lord Duncan joined the British Army and was sent to fight the French in north-east America. At Fort Carillon he learned that the native Americans called the place Ticonderoga. He knew he was going to die and told his friends. In a vicious battle many men died and Lord Duncan received a slight wound from a musket. He felt he had escaped, but ten days later the wound had turned septic. He died and the ghost's revenge was complete.

4. **The Fox family ghost**. A family called Fox lived near New York. There was farmer James Fox, his wife and two daughters, Maggie and Katie. In 1848 their house was disturbed by strange banging noises in the night. The girls discovered they could communicate with a disturbed spirit through

rapping – one rap for "yes", two for "no". Eventually they learned that the rappings came from the spirit of a man called Charles Rosma. Rosma told how he was murdered and buried in the cellar. When neighbours helped the Fox family to dig in the cellar they found human hair and bones. The spirit said he was murdered by a Mr Bell, but that the killer would never be brought to justice. Mr Bell, who had lived in the house five years before the Fox family, was very angry and denied it. The case caused such a sensation in the press that the Fox girls became famous and appeared all over America. The Spiritualist movement started in America and many people copied the performances of the Fox girls. After forty years of fame Katie admitted it was all a trick, but the Spiritualists refused to believe her!

GHOSTLY DREAMS
George's Dream

George and Hart were brothers who lived in Cornwall, England. They were not just brothers but very close friends too.

George became a sailor and they were separated for the first time in their lives. In February 1840 George's ship reached the island of St Helena. While he was there he had a horrific dream. This is his story . . .

Cornwall, England, 1840

I dreamed that my brother, Hart, was at Trebodwina market and that I was with him. I was quite close by his side during the whole of his buying and selling. I could see and hear everything that went on around me. But I felt it wasn't my body that was travelling round with him; it was my shadow or my spirit. Hart didn't seem to know that I was there.

Hart spoke to people and they replied. I could hear it all. But when I tried to speak no one heard me and no one replied.

I felt that this was a sign of some hidden danger that was going to befall him but I knew I wouldn't be able to stop the danger because I had no way of warning him. All I could do was stand by helplessly and watch.

My brother Hart had a very successful day at the market and made a large sum of money. I should have felt happy for him but all I felt was fear. As the sun set he began to make his way homeward on his horse. My shadow followed him and my terror grew as he reached the village of Polkerrow.

Polkerrow is no longer a village. It is just a collection of deserted cottages round the cross-roads. No one lives there now. It was quiet and the setting sun was casting long shadows over the road. I was frantic. I wanted to warn Hart in some way that he must go no further.

Then I noticed two long shadows moving across the path. Two men appeared from one of the deserted cottages. It seemed they had been waiting there. I knew them well – they were the Hightwood brothers. They were villainous poachers who lived in a lonely wood near St Eglos. I also knew that it was Hart they were waiting for.

The men said, "Good evening, master," very politely.

"Good evening," Hart replied. "I had been meaning to call on you," he said. It seemed he didn't sense the danger. My shadow was screaming out, "Ride on! Ride on now before it is too late." But Hart did not hear any warning.

"I have some animals I want taking to market next week," Hart said.

"So why not pay us now, Mr Northey?" the older Hightwood said.

That was the first time Hart began to sense they meant no good.

"I cannot pay for work that has not yet been done," he said.

"Ah, but you can, Mr Northey," the younger Hightwood said. He was standing by my brother's saddle. The older man walked to the horse's head and took hold of the horse's reins. "We need the money now," he said.

"Come to my house and I'll see if I can loan you some," Hart said. The horse could feel my brother's nervousness and started prancing in the dust.

The older man was holding the horse's head firmly. He said, "Mr Northey, we know you have just come from Trebodwina market. And we also know you have plenty of money in your pockets. We are desperate men and you aren't leaving this place until we've got that money. So hand it over."

Hart did not reply. He lashed at the man with his whip and spurred the horse on. The man fell back but held on to the reins.

The younger poacher immediately drew a pistol and fired. He was standing close to my brother's side. He could not miss. I watched as Hart dropped lifeless from the saddle. The poachers tied the horse to a tree in the orchard. Then they stole the money from Hart's pockets and dragged his body up the stream. They hid him under the overhanging bushes.

The poachers returned to the road and covered up the marks on the road. They hid the pistol in the thatched roof of a disused cottage by the roadside and returned home to

their own house in the woods.

My ship left St Helena and sailed for Plymouth. All the way home I was sure that my brother had been murdered in the way I'd seen in my dream. When I reached home two months later my father was waiting at the quayside. "I know what you have come to tell me," I said. "It's Hart, isn't it?"

"Yes," my father said.

"He was robbed and murdered two months ago."

My father nodded. "You were always close to Hart," he said. "It is no surprise that you sensed his death."

And he told me the details of the crime. They were exactly as I had seen in my dream.

"The whole county was shocked by the brutal murder," my father said. "The authorities were determined to bring the murderers to justice. Two poachers called Hightwood have been arrested. Their cottage has been searched and blood-stained clothes found. 'From skinning rabbits,' the brothers claimed. But there was no pistol. The younger

Hightwood said he had owned a gun years ago, but had lost it," he went on.

"The Hightwoods were taken to the magistrates' court. There wasn't much evidence against them. That murder weapon is still missing. But the men acted in a guilty manner. They were sent for trial anyway," my father explained.

"In that case I think I can help avenge my brother's murder. For I can tell you where the gun is hidden. The gun is in the thatch of the cottage by the roadside." I said.

That was George's story. He could have been lying about dreaming the murder – after all, the men had already been arrested and their story was known to everyone.

But when the roof was searched the gun was found, exactly as in the dream.

"How did you know?" George was asked.

"Because I saw it in a dream," he answered.

"And when did you have this dream?"

"I had the dream on the very night my brother was murdered, though I was two thousand miles away."

Faced with the weapon, the Hightwoods confessed to the murder. They hoped that the confession would save their lives and they'd be sent to prison. It didn't work.

A month later they were hanged for their crime.

Ghostly thoughts 6

Doubles: The image of a living person is seen by a friend or relative when they are many miles away. This is usually at a time of trouble for the "double", maybe when they are on the point of death.

Explanation? Perhaps everyone is a mind-reader. As well as seeing, touching, smelling or hearing other people maybe we can also sense their thoughts when those thoughts are very emotional. Our sight and hearing only allow us to sense people so far and no further, but thoughts can travel hundreds or even thousands of miles.

Ghostly Visions – FACT FILE

In the story of the Northey brothers the "ghost" was the living *relative. His spirit seems to have left his body and travelled thousands of miles to be at the scene of the crime.*

Another type of ghostly vision is when the ghost of the dead *person visits a relative (or friend or loved one) at the time of their death. These ghost stories are called "point of death" visions. Many thousands have been recorded over the years . . .*

1. **The Last Goodbye**. Rod Nielson lived in San Diego in California. He was very close to his father, Henry. Old Henry loved his grand-daughter Katie but seemed sad when he heard that Rod's wife was having another grandchild. He hinted that he wouldn't be around to see his new grandson. He was quite, quite sure that the unborn baby would be a boy. In the summer of 1972 Rod was in his office when he clearly heard his father say, "Well, I guess that's it, son. Give Katie a kiss from me. Goodbye." Rod turned and saw an image of his father in a checked shirt and old trousers. In Henry's hand was a garden trowel and a bunch of marigolds. No one else in the office saw a thing. Rod hurried to his father's house. Henry was lying dead on the lawn wearing the same

clothes as in the vision. In one hand he held a garden trowel, in the other a bunch of marigolds. But that's not the end of the story. For when the baby was born it *was* a boy. Rod turned to young Katie and said, "Pity Granddad couldn't be here to see it." Katie shook her head, "But Daddy," she said, "Granddad *is* here, standing next to Mummy. Can't you see him?"

2. **The Tugboat disaster**. Not all ghosts appear at the "moment of death". Mrs Paquet of Chicago walked into her pantry and saw a clear image of her brother. He appeared to trip over a rope and vanish over a low railing. She knew that he was working on a tugboat in Chicago Harbour at the time. Mrs Paquet dropped her cup of tea and cried, "My God! Ed is drowned!" She eventually received news that this had in fact happened, but it had happened six hours before her vision.

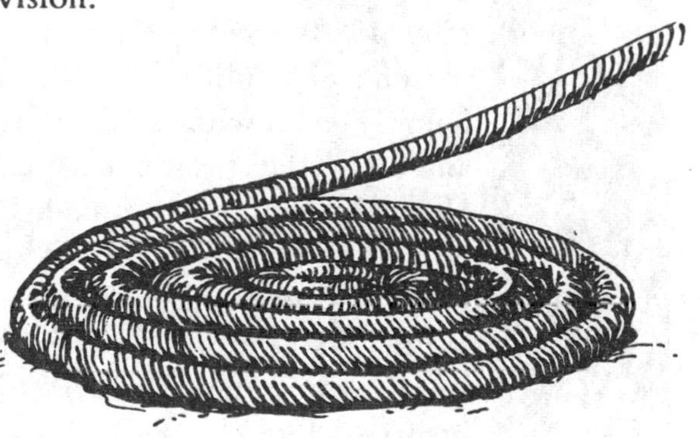

3. **The Woman in White**. One of the most chilling ghosts must be the one that foretells your own death. In 1837 John Allen saw something which told him he was about to die. He was miserable for the next six months but he would never say why. Then, one day while he was at work, his daughter Polly saw a woman dressed in white walking down the hill towards her. No one else saw the woman and Polly's sister laughed at her. "People don't wear white dresses on a working day," she said. Later that day they learned that their father had drowned while he was working on the river. He died at the time Polly had seen the woman. She had not seen the dying person at the moment of his death, as in most stories, but had she seen the ghost her father had met just months before?

4. **The Ghostly Car**. At 11.30 p.m. on 4 May 1980, Joseph Hannah's father heard Joseph's car pull into the driveway at their home. He knew the sound of that car engine and the sounds his son made parking his car. He fell asleep, content that his son was home safely. At 11.30 p.m. on 4 May 1980 Joseph Hannah's girlfriend saw him driving down the main street of her town. He waved and smiled at her, then drove on. She was a little surprised because she had watched him set off home at 11 p.m. At 11.30 p.m. on 4 May

1980 Joseph Hannah's baby-sitter heard footsteps pacing in the baby's room. Three people thought they'd seen or heard Joseph at 11.30 that night, but none of them had. He had died at 11.10 that evening when his car was wrecked by a landslide.

5. **The White Room**. Some vision stories have a happy ending. In the 1850s a little girl was walking along a country lane not far from her home. Slowly the lane faded from sight and all she could see was a bedroom in her house known as the White Room. Her mother was lying, still, on the floor. Instead

of going home the girl went straight to the doctor and persuaded him to go home with her. They found her mother, in the White Room, suffering from a heart attack. The doctor saved her life. It seems as if the mother's spirit had carried a "panic" message to her daughter.

GHOSTLY RETURNS
The Lives and Deaths of Jane

Have you ever visited a place and felt that you've been there before, even though you know you haven't? Many people have that feeling. One explanation is that you really have *been there before . . . in another life. Perhaps we have all lived many lives before, but we've forgotten them. However, if we are hypnotized we might just remember our past lives . . .*

Cardiff, Wales, 1974

"I shall count slowly backwards from ten. When I reach zero you will be asleep. Do you understand?"

The woman nodded. Her feet were up on the couch but she wasn't relaxed. Her bright eyes were fixed on the old man. "Yes, doctor," she said. Her voice was thin with a musical Welsh accent.

He looked at her. "No, Jane, not yet. You're still a little too excited. You've been hypnotized many times before. You know you have to relax."

She closed her eyes and took a deep breath. After a minute she said, "I'm ready."

The man's voice was smooth and soothing as he began to count slowly. "Ten . . . your eyelids are heavy . . . nine . . . you can feel them closing . . . eight . . . you are going to sleep . . . seven . . . all you can hear is my voice . . . six . . . your body is so heavy it is sinking through the couch . . . five . . . your breathing is slower . . . four . . . you will be asleep when I say 'zero' . . . three . . . but you will still hear my voice . . . two . . . you are slipping . . . one . . . zero."

Jane's eyes were closed, her mouth slightly open and her body limp. The man spoke briskly. "Now, Jane, we have done this before. I'm going to ask you to go back in time. Back to the days before you were born. Back to when you lived another life in another body. Do you remember?"

"Yes-s," she replied with a tired slur to her voice.

"But this time will be different, won't it?"

"Yes."

"In the past I have told you which date I wanted you to return to. We went back to Roman Britain, didn't we?"

"Yes . . . I was called Livonia," the woman said dreamily.

"And in Tudor England you were the maid of honour to a princess," the man went on. His eyes behind the spectacles were sharp as a bird's.

"This time I want *you* to choose. Of all the lives you've lived before, is there one that stands out in your memory?"

The woman's limp face tensed in a frown. Her soft breathing became harsh and her limp hands were clenched into fists. The white-haired man leaned forward. "Let it happen, Jane . . . relax."

As he watched the woman changed. Her face became alive and her eyes flew open. The slack chin grew tight and she lifted it proudly.

The man asked, "Who are you?"

"Rebecca," the woman replied quickly. Her voice was firm and there was no trace of the Welsh accent Jane had.

"Where do you live, Rebecca?"

"York," she said.

"The year?"

"In Christian years it is 1189."

"Tell me about your life," he urged softly.

The Rebecca character spoke quickly as if she were irritated by the questions, or too busy to stop and answer them. "It's such a hard life for us."

"You're poor?"

Her lips pursed in anger. "Of course not. My husband is a wealthy merchant. It's hard because we're Jewish."

"I see," the old man nodded and sat back a little.

"They hate us," she said and an angry spot of red coloured each cheek. "The Christians can't lend money . . . it's against the law . . . but we Jews can. They come to us to borrow and they hate us because they owe us. They make us wear yellow badges on our clothes. They hate us. The Christians blame us for everything. Two hundred of them died in a plague last summer, but no Jews died. They say that is our fault too. They want to kill us!"

"Why do you say that?"

"There were riots in London and Lincoln and Chester. They killed Jews then. York will be next. I fear for my children. My little Rachel is only eleven. What will happen to her?"

The woman twisted her hands in worry and her face was creased with suffering.

The man leaned forward and spoke slowly. "Rebecca, time has moved on. When we last spoke you were worried about being attacked. What has happened?"

Now the woman's face was pale. Her eyes were staring. "Hush! Keep your voice down. They will hear us."

"Sorry," the man said quietly. "Where are you?"

"We are in the Christian church near Coppergate, hiding in a cellar. If they find us they will murder us."

"What happened?"

"We woke to the smell of burning . . . they'd come in the night and set fire to Benjamin's house next door. They killed his wife and children and carried off all his treasure. So we put all our money in bags and fled to the castle for safety."

"Did you reach it?"

"They followed us. Through the dark streets they chased us. They were carrying torches and screaming they wanted us burned. My husband, Joseph, took a knife and split a sack of money. The silver spilled out on the road. The mob stopped to pick it up. We reached the castle and we stood inside with all the other Jews of York."

"The mob couldn't get you in the castle," the hypnotist said.

"Oh, but they could. They began battering at the door. Some parents began to kill their own children rather than let the mob get their hands on them."

"But you didn't kill Rachel?"

"No. Oh, no. We used the last of our money to bribe a guard. He let us out of a secret door before the mob broke down the gates. Now we're hiding in this church. They tell us King John has ordered the murder of all Jews in England! It's not just the people who are chasing us now, it's the soldiers too. Joseph has gone for food. He's been such a long time. Now Rachel is crying – hush, Rachel, they'll hear us! Listen! Horses. I can hear horses."

"Perhaps it's Joseph returning with food," the white-haired man said.

"Joseph didn't have a horse. No . . . I can hear their footsteps now. They're coming for us. They're shouting, 'Kill the Jews, kill the Jews!' They're searching the church now. God protect us! Hush, Rachel, don't cry. Only the priest knows we're down here. A priest will not betray us . . . but listen . . . I can hear the sound of the stone floor being lifted. He's told them where we are . . . they're coming . . . no, not Rachel! Not my Rachel! Don't take my child . . . no-o-o!" the woman wailed, a long and terrified cry.

The hypnotist was shocked. "They haven't taken her, have they? They're not going to harm you, are they?"

But the woman's tortured face was blank now. Her eyes stared, sightless. She whispered just one word. So soft that the man hardly heard it. "Dark," she sighed.

The man was trembling a little as he said, "Jane? Jane?"

The woman on the couch was limp again. Her eyes closed.

"Jane, I'm going to count to three. On the count of three you will wake up. You will be Jane Evans and the year is 1974. One . . . two . . . three!"

The woman opened her eyes slowly. She smiled at the

man and her voice was bright with that Welsh accent. "What happened, doctor?" she said. "Why, doctor, are you all right? Was it something I said? You look like *death*!"

Ghostly thoughts 7

Reincarnation: Many people believe that they have lived on earth before. Some religions say that your body dies but your soul comes back over and over again. This is called reincarnation.

Explanation? a) Jane read a book about the massacre then forgot she'd read it. When she was hypnotized all the details were unlocked from her memory;
b) Jane's spirit really had once lived (and died) in Rebecca's body.

Ghostly Returns – FACT FILE

Some people have seen their past lives in dreams or under hypnosis. But are they real? There are arguments for and against.

The case for reincarnation

1. Jane Evans' story was checked by a historian. Many of the facts were correct, and they were the sort of things an ordinary housewife like Jane would not know. Where did she get the facts from if she didn't get them from the memory of a past life?
2. "Rebecca" described hiding in the cellar of a church near Coppergate in York. But historians said the church nearest Coppergate had no cellar. Then, six months after Jane Evans' tape was made, workmen found a cellar just where she'd said it was. How could she have known about the cellar when no one else in this century knew?
3. Some people claim that they learn things in one life and keep that skill in their next life. A man who was a great piano player died. His spirit then entered the body of a baby who grew up to be a brilliant piano player at the age of three years old! That baby was the famous musician, Mozart. How else did he learn so quickly?

The case against reincarnation

1. An investigator looked closely into Jane Evans's story and decided that much of her information was incorrect about York and Jews of that time. The researcher also discovered that a lot of her information came from a play that had been broadcast on BBC Radio.

2. Another of Jane Evans' "characters" was Livonia, who lived in Roman Britain. Much of her story came word for word from a novel called *The Living Wood* by Louis de Wohl. It seems Jane forgot that she'd read the book but the details were there in the back of her mind. This is something called "secret memory" that everybody seems to have.

3. A lot of the remembered "characters" are famous people with interesting stories to tell. Surely the chances of being a king or a queen must be millions to one. A 1980s tour guide in Egypt once complained that, in the dozens of American tourists on that trip, he had *nine* Cleopatras!

GHOSTLY MESSENGERS

Diary of a Haunting

Some ghosts seem doomed to wander the earth because they need to tell someone something before they leave. It can take years – hundreds of years – before they find the right person to listen. Not everyone can "tune in" to a ghost. It seems that some people, especially nervous people, can attract a ghost to tell its story. In the case of the haunting at Ash Manor in Sussex the ghost had a long wait before it found the right person . . .

The Diary of Elizabeth Keller,
aged 16 years and three months

23 June 1934

Our last night in the old house. I do hope we'll be happy in the new one. It's called Ash Manor and it is beautiful. Father took us to see it yesterday. So peaceful. I'm sure father and mother will be happier once we settle in.

It's been hard for them, I know. Father's been so miserable. I'm not sure quite why. The doctor says it's something called "depression". I think it's the strain of running his business. Everyone is having trouble making money these days. I think that's why the last owners of Ash Manor sold it; they needed the money. Anyway, Father says it was very cheap.

Once we move in he'll have that lovely old house to come home to at night.

I can't wait.

24 June 1934

The end of our first day. The servants have been working very hard to make the house ready for us. It's so large I have my own bedroom and writing room. That's where I'm writing this diary.

The vicar, Mr Twist, said the oldest part of Ash Manor dates back to the thirteenth century and the reign of Edward the Confessor. I know from my history lessons that Edward the Confessor was king in the eleventh century. But it would have been rude to correct the good man so I held my tongue.

Most of the house is only about a hundred years old, though. Mr Twist says the original building began to crumble and was rebuilt by a Victorian owner. But I live in the oldest part.

It's so thrilling to know I'm surrounded by six hundred (or eight hundred) years of history! Hope I'm not too excited to sleep.

25 June 1934

I'm tired. I didn't sleep too well. I know the servants still had lots of unpacking and sorting to do, but I didn't expect them to be up half of the night doing it.

I spoke to the maid quite sharply at breakfast.

"Metcalfe."

"Yes, Miss Keller?" she said.

"What time did you get to bed last night?"

"I beg your pardon?" she said, surprised.

"I heard you moving about in the servants' quarters till all hours," I complained.

She couldn't look me in the face. Her hand was shaking as she served my scrambled egg. "Sorry, Miss, but we was all asleep by midnight," she muttered.

Metcalfe was lying, of course. I could tell that father had been disturbed by them too. His face was grey with fatigue and there were purplish shadows under his eyes.

He seemed very much withdrawn. Hardly spoke. I'm

sure he'll be better when he's settled in and had a good night's sleep.

Mother and I explored the gardens of Ash Manor today. They'll be beautiful when the gardeners have finished. A fine place to sit and read. We had tea on the lawn, though it needs cutting.

Father was late home from work and we have all gone to bed early. I hope I sleep better tonight.

26 June 1934

Another night with very little sleep, and everyone's nerves are getting frayed. I got out of bed at midnight to climb to the servants' quarters and complain about their tramping about in the middle of the night. But the servants were nowhere to be seen. The sounds were those of footsteps on floorboards and they seemed to be coming from the attic.

This morning I asked Almond, the butler, about the footsteps.

"No, Miss Keller, there are no floorboards in the attic," he said. "The servants heard nothing," he added quickly. But I know he's lying. They're trying to hide something. When father came down he looked worse than ever. I asked him about it.

"Nothing to bother yourself about, Elizabeth," he said.

But when I persisted, he said, "The servants seem to think the place is haunted. They've been talking to the shopkeepers in the village about some old legends. All nonsense, of course. The last people to live here had no problems – and they lived here for seven years. And the ones before for thirteen. It's all nonsense. Probably just jackdaws roosting in the attic. We'll get someone to sort them out. Now get on with your breakfast." But I wasn't hungry.

I asked Mr Twist, the vicar, about the stories and he laughed. But it wasn't a very happy laugh. He made some excuse and left very quickly.

27 June 1934

I'm so tired. I don't think I slept more than two hours. I'd fallen asleep at ten o'clock but was wakened at midnight by the most terrible fuss in the corridor outside the bedroom. Father was standing at the door to Mother's room and babbling something. I ran across and said, "What's wrong?"

"Help me get him into the library," Mother said, and we led him downstairs. Mother poured him a large glass of brandy and made him drink it while I rubbed his cold and shaking hand.

"Go back to bed, Elizabeth," Mother ordered.

"No, let her stay," Father put in. "She needs to hear this too. She's sixteen now, you know."

"I know how old my daughter is, thank you," Mother snapped. "I simply think we should not burden her with the problems of your nerves."

Father looked up angrily and I was afraid they were going to start one of their terrible rows. His breathing was short and tense but he kept his voice low. "It was not my nerves, Alice," he said. "You admit you heard it too!"

Mother gave a sharp nod. Father turned to me. "I was lying awake, reading, when I heard the most fearful bangs on my door. Three bangs. But when I opened it there was no one there. I went to your mother's room. She heard them too. I didn't imagine it. There is nothing wrong with my nerves. Nothing. Nothing!"

"Of course not, Father," I soothed him.

But none of us could get back to sleep.

28 June 1934

And now my father has seen it. This time I heard the knock on his door. I hurried from my room and saw my father standing there, clinging to the doorpost in fear. When we got him into the library this time he said, "I've seen him . . . it . . . I've seen the thing that's been making the noise."

"Hush!" Mother said. "You'll frighten Elizabeth."

"I need to know," I said. "Go on, Father. What was it?"

He swallowed thirstily at the brandy and let out a low sigh. "Standing in the doorway was a man. An oldish man – older than me, dressed in one of those things peasants used to wear on farms."

"A smock," my mother said.

"Aye, a smock. A green smock. And his trousers were muddy, as if he'd just come from the fields. He had a shapeless hat on his head and a sort of scarf around his throat. I thought it was one of the gardeners. I asked him what he wanted. He didn't seem to hear me. Didn't answer. So I went to grab his shoulder, but my hand went clean through it. I fell back against the doorpost almost in a faint. When I opened my eyes again he'd gone."

"We'll see what Mr Twist has to say about this," Mother said. "The vicar will soon rid us of this . . . thing."

I was surprised. Mother has always blamed my father's "nerves" for everything. "You think there is something, Mother?" I asked carefully.

She looked at me and her eyes were dark-shadowed like

father's. "I . . . I heard the knock too."

"You went to your door?"

"I went to my door," she said.

"And you saw the ghost?"

Perhaps I shouldn't have used that word. Mother's lips went pale and tight. "I saw . . . something," she admitted. "I saw it walk towards the fireplace in your father's room. I'm sure there's something hidden in that chimney."

"What else, Mother?" I asked.

"It raised its head . . . I saw what lay beneath that scarf around its neck."

"What was it, Mother?"

She looked at me. "Pray you never see it, child!"

2 July 1934

So much has happened I haven't had the time to keep this diary up to date. Mr Twist came with his prayers and sprinkling of holy water. "Exorcism," he called it. That seemed to annoy the ghost. It's becoming bolder. I have seen it for myself.

So have the servants and that is why Metcalfe is leaving. We are becoming desperate, so desperate that we have called in a spiritualist – someone who can talk to spirits, see who it is, find out what it wants.

I sleep in Mother's bedroom now and we pray. That seems to help. I hope this spiritualist can end our misery.

4 July 1934

Mr Twist said it is mumbo-jumbo. He doesn't believe in spiritualism. But it was so amazing. The medium was Mrs Garrett, a small Irish woman about Mother's age.

She walked in the front door and stopped. "Ah, yes," she said. "I can feel the problem."

"Poppycock!" Mr Twist muttered, but she ignored him.

"There is pain. There is suffering here," she said. She had a slight Irish accent.

Mrs Garrett wandered round the house then came to the oldest part. "Here," she said. "We will try to talk to him here."

"What should we do?" Father asked nervously.

"Sit around the table," she ordered. "Draw the curtains."

"That'll be so we can't see any tricks or jiggery-pokery," Mr Twist whispered to me.

When we were sitting in the gloom lit by just one candle, Mrs Garrett said she had a link with the world of spirits, in particular a spirit called Uvani. We should not be bothered if she seemed to change during the session.

She closed her eyes. All I could hear was Mr Twist's breathing. Even he was fascinated. At last Mrs Garret opened her eyes. When she spoke her voice was stronger and she had no Irish accent. It seems it was the spirit of Uvani speaking to us.

"There is a man who wishes to speak to you. The man who is haunting this house."

"Who is he?" mother said quickly.

"His name is Charles Edward . . . and he has suffered much from imprisonment," Mrs Garrett (or Uvani) replied.

"Was he imprisoned here?" Mr Twist put in. "This house was never a prison."

Uvani seemed to be talking to Charles Edward a few moments then spoke to us. "No. The prison was near here but not in this house."

"Then why does he come here?" the vicar asked.

"Charles Edward is suffering and he felt some living soul suffering in this house. Suffering attracts suffering like a magnet."

We knew Uvani meant Father and his nervous problem. We said nothing.

"Who imprisoned him?" Mr Twist asked.

"The king – King Edward, his half-brother," Uvani replied.

"Which King Edward? The fourth or the fifth?"

Uvani nodded and simply said, "Yes."

"Hah! That's a nonsense reply," the vicar snapped. That seemed to destroy the spell. The spiritualist blinked and the spirit of Uvani left her.

Mrs Garrett will return tomorrow and then we speak to Charles Edward himself.

5 July 1934

Mrs Garrett's face changed when Charles Edward took over her body. We all gasped. For her face became the face of the man in green, and her voice was a man's voice. "A trick," Mr Twist said. I wasn't so sure. Charles Edward spoke.

"I am half-brother to the king, but my followers believe I have more right to the throne than Edward. They started a rebellion and put me at the head. I didn't really want the crown, I just wanted my land back. I was robbed of my land by the Earl of Huntingdon. Of course Edward won. He locked me up here and left me to rot in gaol."

"Which king?" Mr Twist said softly.

"Edward."

"Which Edward?"

"Edward," was all the spirit would say.

"Why do you haunt this house?" the vicar asked.

"I need help – help me to take my revenge. Revenge on the friends who betrayed me; revenge on the brother who tortured me."

"They are all dead," Mr Twist said. "Long, long dead."

"I want my revenge!" the spirit cried and it brought tears to my eyes to hear him. To me he was as real a person as Mother or Father. "I will not leave until I have had my revenge."

Father gave a great sigh and buried his face in his hands. "We'll never be free of this haunting."

6 July 1934

I do not like Mr Twist, but he spoke a lot of sense today.

"The woman is a fraud," he said. "She makes money by putting on performances like she did last night."

"We paid her well," Mother admitted.

"I know a lot of local history," the vicar went on. "Mrs Garret's story was a powerful one, but a nonsense. Did you notice how she refused to name the king? I have checked all the record books and this rebellion simply never happened."

"So what is this ghost? We didn't imagine him. We've all seen him. Another servant left today," Mother said.

"I think Mrs Garrett said one thing that made sense. She said that suffering attracts suffering. Mr Keller is clearly unhappy. It is his unhappiness which is creating the haunting. This house is haunted because Mr Keller wants it to be haunted."

I looked at Father. He didn't deny it. "But who is the green man?"

"The green man is not the long-lost brother of a long-dead king. The green man only lived in one place. He was created in the mind of your unhappy father. Once your father finds happiness the green man will disappear." The vicar turned to Father. "See a doctor, Mr Keller, then come to church and find peace." He turned to Mother and me. "And you have your parts to play. Suffering attracts suffering – but remember, happiness attracts happiness. Be happy."

We talked long into the night. We resolved to try. We will help one another. Together we can destroy this ghostly green man.

7 July 1934

Last night I slept peacefully for the first time since we moved here. The green man is gone, driven away by the one weapon he couldn't face. Happiness.

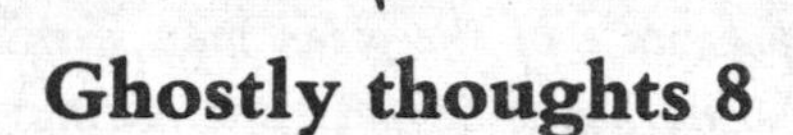

Ghostly thoughts 8

Spirits: The "souls" of dead people who don't want to leave this world. The spirit wants to talk to a friend or relative by a) appearing as a vision (often in a dream) and giving a message; b) finding a sensitive person to carry their message – a "medium". They speak through the mouth of that medium. Sometimes these spirits are friendly and want to pass on advice or warnings to their loved ones.

Explanation? The living may simply dream the vision. Many "mediums" have been caught out in their cheating over the years. Remember, they are often well paid!

Fakes – FACT FILE

The Ash Manor case is interesting. The ghostly appearance of the green man seems to be a truly ghostly happening, but the attempt to talk to the ghost through a "medium" seems to have been a trick.

In the history of ghosts there have been a lot of tricksters making a lot of money from frauds and fakes. Some unhappy people want to talk to a loved one who is dead. A "medium" will claim to put them in touch with the dead person and pass on messages, but could simply pretend to pass on their messages and invent the replies they want to hear.

In Ancient Greece you could talk to the gods through the "medium" of a priest and receive replies. Even today mediums can fill large theatres with hundreds of people who believe they are in touch with the afterlife.

Sadly there is a long history of fakes.

1. **The ghostbuster**. Harry Houdini was a very skilled magician whose special trick was escaping – from handcuffs, boxes, coffins, safes and even prisons. Houdini desperately wanted to get in touch with his dead mother. He spent years looking for a genuine medium but all he found were fakes. Being a great magician himself he could work out all the tricks they used.

2. **The ghostly cabinet**. The American Davenport Brothers used a special cabinet in their performances in the 1860s. They were tied up and locked in the cabinet. On the darkened stage ghostly hands reached from the cabinet and played musical instruments. When the cabinet was opened they were found to be tied up as tightly as ever. Many people saw this as proof of a spirit world and no one ever caught them trying to cheat. A religion called Spiritualism grew up in the nineteenth century from such contacts with the dead. Many other mediums began to copy the cabinet idea. Before Ira Davenport died he confessed to Harry Houdini that it was all a clever fraud, and showed him the conjuring tricks the brothers had used.

3. **The fairy photographs**. Sir Arthur Conan Doyle was the writer of the Sherlock Holmes detective stories and a great believer in spiritualism. He was shown photographs of fairies taken by two girls in Yorkshire. He was quite sure that the photographs proved that fairies existed and never considered that two girls aged ten and sixteen could create cunning trick photographs. Doyle and thousands of others believed the pictures were real. They weren't! The "fairies" in the pictures were paper cutouts. The sisters finally admitted their trick sixty years later, long after Doyle's death.

4. **The solid ghost**. Mediums can produce rapping noises and make tables rise from the floor. But their most amazing skill is to make a ghost "materialize" – take a solid form and walk round the room. The medium will usually step inside a cabinet and close the curtains. In the darkened room a spot of white will appear in front of the curtains and grow into a cloud. A face will emerge from the cloud and finally the whole ghost. The ghost can walk around the room and touch the visitors, who may find the spirit solid and warm. An author called Robert Chaney explained that the solid ghost is formed from "ectoplasm" – part of the medium's own body flows out of her mouth and forms a second body that the ghost steps into. The truth is that the solid "ghost" is just the medium in a different dress. The top dress is taken off behind the curtains; the medium is wearing a second one painted in luminous paint underneath. The "cloud" is a piece of fine white material that the medium has hidden, usually in her knickers!

Perhaps the most famous case of fraud is the Cock Lane ghost of the 1760s in London . . .

POLTERGEISTS
The Cock Lane Ghost

Most ghosts are harmless. Miserable to themselves, frightening to other people, but harmless.

The only sorts of ghosts that seem dangerous are "poltergeists". A poltergeist is a spirit that often begins by making rapping noises but gradually gets more violent. Objects are thrown around a room and people may be lifted into the air.

Many poltergeists have one thing in common. They appear in a room where a teenager is living. Some scientists say the poltergeist is in fact the spirit of that teenager. Because the young person is growing up they lose control of the spirit inside them. This "out of control spirit" is so strong it can move objects. The trouble is that because it is "out of control" the teenager can't "switch on" the poltergeist whenever s/he wants. That means it can't be tested very easily.

If you were a teenager with poltergeist problems you'd get a lot of attention. If you enjoyed that attention then you might want the disturbances to go on. How do you do that? Sometimes you have to cheat. The trouble is, if you are caught cheating just once then no one will ever believe there was a true poltergeist spirit.

That's what happened to little Lizzie Parsons . . .

London, England, 1762

The room was dim. It was hot. There were too many people crowded in it to meet the famous Cock Lane Ghost.

They shuffled and sniffed, they coughed and they muttered the odd word here and there. Some sat on chairs around the bed. Some stood. No one leaned against the wooden walls. They'd heard the stories. There was something there, behind the walls. Something strange and menacing.

There was a bed against one wall, and in the bed lay a

girl of about thirteen – a small girl with wide eyes over a snub nose and pale cheeks. Lizzie Parsons.

A thin man in a black coat spoke quietly. "The ghost will be here soon, ladies and gentlemen," he said. He said it for the fifth time. Someone sighed.

"It's not there, Pa," the girl said. "Too many people in the room, I think."

Some people groaned and grumbled.

"Sorry, I'll have to ask you to leave," Richard Parsons said.

There was a clattering of chairs and louder grumbles as the watchers rose and wandered out of the door. Finally there were just three men in the room with Richard Parsons and his daughter, Lizzie.

The large man with a red face turned to Richard Parsons. "So they are all lies, are they? All these stories you've been spreading about me are lies, eh?"

Parsons wrung his hands. "I've said nothing about you, Will Kent. It's the spirit. The spirit has been saying those things. You can't blame me!"

"But I do blame you, Parsons," the big man said, and his face turned a darker red. "I even read about myself in the newspaper. Read about the things you said I'd done."

Will Kent took a step forward and Parsons backed away. The big man's hand clenched into a fist. He began to raise it. Parsons whimpered and turned his head away. Suddenly there was a sharp noise.

Rap!

Will Kent looked round quickly. The two men who were with him shrugged their shoulders. "The spirit!" Parsons squeaked. "The spirit is ready to speak! Sit down, Kent; sit down Minister; sit down, Doctor." Parsons fussed them like a hen with chicks until they were seated in a half-circle round the bed.

Little Lizzie lay perfectly still in the bed, her eyes fixed on the ceiling. Her father spoke quietly but clearly. "Are you there, spirit?"

Rap!

"That means, 'yes'," Parsons explained quickly. "It's two raps for 'no'."

The visitors looked around the room. The noise seemed to have come from the wall behind them. The minister crossed himself quickly. The doctor looked puzzled. Kent looked at Parsons with hatred.

"Oh, spirit, have you a message for us?" Parsons asked.

Rap!

"Will you tell us who you are, spirit?"

Rap!

"Are you the spirit of Will Kent's wife?"

Rap!

"His first wife?"

Rap Rap!

"His second wife, Frances?"

Rap!

"We wish to know how you died, Frances. Did you die naturally?"

Rap! Rap!

"Then, were you murdered?"

Rap!

"Who murdered you, Frances? Was it your husband Will Kent here?"

RAP!

There was a louder clatter as Kent jumped to his feet and the chair crashed to the floor. "You lie, spirit! You lie!

I know I didn't kill my Frances. That's the truth," he roared.

The doctor put a hand on his shoulder to calm him. Kent tore it away. He pointed a thick finger at Parsons. "This ghost must repeat the accusation in front of a magistrate. If it doesn't then you'll suffer for this, Parsons."

"It's not *my* fault," the thin man cringed. "The spirit –"

"It is *your* spirit! You are doing this to get me hanged for killing my wife. The way I see it, Parsons, you are trying to kill me. You are the murderer. And the penalty for attempted murder is death."

"But –" Parsons began to object. Kent and his two friends were already out of the door and pushing through the crowds who had huddled outside to hear the argument.

"We'll just have to prove ourselves in front of a magistrate, Lizzie," the thin man said to his daughter.

"I'll try, Pa," the girl said from her bed. "I'll try."

News of the ghost spread through the streets of London. Crowds gathered at Cock Lane the next day to get a glimpse of the spirit. In the local tavern the landlord Franzen served beer to the crowds. The beer was dearer than usual, but they got their money's worth. "A thin, pale ghost it was. Saw her with my own eyes. Wandering past the window of the house. Wailing and crying."

"When was that, landlord?" someone asked.

"That would be Christmas 1759," Franzen said.

"Then you can't have seen the ghost of Mrs Kent – she didn't die till the February of 1760," the man argued.

The landlord gave a wide, smug smile that showed the blackened stumps of rotting teeth. "Ahh . . . but the *first* Mrs Kent died two years before that."

The crowd gathered closer round the beer barrel. "You

mean he murdered *her* as well?"

The landlord narrowed his red-rimmed eyes. "Arsenic poison in her beer, same as the second Mrs Kent," he said.

"You think the spirit will speak to the magistrate?" someone asked.

"It has to," Franzen said. "It has to."

And a week later Richard Parsons was saying the same thing to little Lizzie. "It has to appear today, Lizzie. Do you understand?"

"Yes, Pa," she said, and there was a tremble of fear in her voice.

"The magistrate will be here in a minute. Are you comfortable?"

"Yes, Pa."

"Good. Then I'll let them into the room. That spirit has to appear today or I'm in trouble, understand?"

"Yes, Pa," the girl murmured and gripped something under the bedclothes.

"Come in, gentlemen," Richard Parsons said. He was twisting a handkerchief in his thin hands.

The magistrate looked at him severely. "You know, Parsons, that it is a serious offence to accuse a man of murder?"

"Oh, yes, your honour. But I'm not accusing anyone. It's the spirit."

"We'll see," Will Kent said as he stepped into the room behind the magistrate.

The two men sat down while Richard Parsons turned towards the bed. "Spirit, are you there?"

This time there was no delay. There was a sharp rap. It seemed to come from the floor under the bed. Will Kent leaned forward. This wasn't the same strange sound that came from the walls before. "Are you the spirit of Frances Kent?" Parsons asked.

Rap!

Kent edged forward again. "Were you murdered, Frances?" Parsons was asking.

Rap!

Will Kent jumped to his feet and snatched the cover off the bed. Lizzie Parsons was lying there in a grubby white night-dress on even grubbier sheets. The big man picked her up easily and dragged her towards the magistrates' chair.

"Show the gentleman what you have in your hand, Lizzie," he shouted.

The terrified girl raised her hand. It held a heavy piece of wood. Kent snatched it and waved it under the magistrate's nose. "Your spirit, I think."

"Richard Parsons, you are under arrest," the magistrate said solemnly. "You are charged with conspiring to bring about the death of William Kent. You will appear before a court tomorrow to answer the charges."

Parsons looked at his daughter.

"Sorry, Pa. I thought that's what you wanted," she said miserably.

All the newspapers of the day wrote about the fraud. None of them were interested in exploring the strange, true happenings before the fraud.

Parsons got two years in jail, four sessions locked in a pillory, and a lot of sympathy. Being locked in the pillory could be a cruel punishment; a man had been stoned to death in the same pillory by angry crowds. When Parsons appeared in the pillory the crowd collected money for him!

It seems some people are determined to believe in ghosts even when fakes have been uncovered. The Cock Lane Ghost was the first time a ghost story had been properly investigated in England.

Would you *be able to tell the difference between a real ghost and a fraud if you had the chance? Over the years ghost hunters have drawn up a series of "rules" to try to help people make sensible decisions about ghosts . . .*

Ghost Hunting – FACT FILE

Good ghost-hunters will attempt to prove a ghost exists by taking some sort of recording equipment, and will go to the site of a reported haunting prepared for anything.

Ghost-hunting Equipment

Ghost hunters will equip themselves with the following:

- Recording equipment (see ghost-hunting rules)
- Torches (plus spare bulbs and batteries)
- Candles (to test for draughts)
- Thermometer (to check if that chill running down the spine is just fear)
- Compass (to check the direction of a sighting or to sense magnetic change in the site)
- Warm and waterproof clothing
- Food and drink
- Notebook and pens/pencils (to record experiences while they're fresh in the mind)
- Talcum powder (scattered on the floor to test for footprints. Sugar has the same effect but also gives a "crunching" sound to warn of unexpected movement.)
- Thread (stretched across corridors or stairs to catch people who are trying to

fake a ghostly appearance)

- Maps and plans of a place are helpful, especially if they show underground streams and mine tunnels or buried power cables

Ghost hunters can prepare by taking the right equipment. But they also need to follow certain rules if they are going to increase their chances of proving ghosts exist.

Ghost-hunting Rules

1 Hunt in pairs

You may be told that a headless horseman haunts a wood. You go to the wood *expecting to see a headless horseman*. Your imagination *tells* you there is a headless horseman on that path ahead of you. You really believe you see it! A good ghost-hunter will take at least one other person. That second person should know as little as possible about the reports so that they *do not know what to expect*.

2 Take recording equipment

A ghost-hunter is looking for *proof*. The more records you have the better. These records can be

- photographs
- video or film
- tape-recorded sound
- footprints
- temperature changes

3 Be patient

Ghosts don't appear very often or very regularly. If you don't see anything in a graveyard on a particular night then you may have been there on the wrong night. Ghost-hunters often have to try over and over again; they don't give up easily.

4 Look for sensible explanations first

Most ghost reports are simple mistakes: strange knocking sounds that turn out to be central heating pipes; pale phantoms that are simply wisps of fog; eerie lights that are reflections of moonlight on a window. The majority of ghost reports are the result of mistakes.

5 Know the haunt

If you are going to spend a night in a castle then spend as much time as possible getting to know it in the daytime. Ghost-hunters should be able to find their way around even on the darkest nights.

6 Believe no one

Don't believe any report until you have checked it for yourself. People who report the ghost to you could be wrong. They could even be lying. In the history of ghost reports there are a lot of fakers, frauds and liars.

7 Know the history of the place

Try to find out as much about the site of the haunting as possible. You need to find out what was there *before* the building existed. Old maps and local history books from the nearest library might help. Then you need to know as much as possible about the people who used to live in the building. Lastly, you need to talk to people who've lived in the area for a long time; what have they heard or seen?

8 Don't be frightened

That's easy to say, of course! But you have to remember that ghosts rarely harm anyone. There are reports of damage to furniture and to rooms but not to people.

9 Don't move

If something appears then don't move until it disappears, making a note of exactly how it vanishes. Is it through a wall? Try to move to the other side of the wall to see if it appears there. Does it go through a door? Then follow it.

10 Don't speak

Ghosts don't usually talk. It seems as if they move in a world of their own and can't see us. But talking can disturb the conditions and cause them to disappear.

EPILOGUE

Do you believe in ghosts?

When someone asks you that perhaps the best answer is to reply, "What sort of ghosts?" There have been several types described in this book. Some are more likely than others.

Did you know . . .

Most ghosts are not *seen*, but people report

- a sound
- a smell
- a feeling of heat or cold
- a feeling of terror
- mysterious movement of objects
- strange lights or shadows

Ghosts are not something you should worry about. Most "ghostly" experiences turn out to have a natural explanation. (In fact some ghost-hunters reckon that out of every 100 reports only two turn out to be truly unexplained.)

You've read some of the millions of ghost stories that people have told about ghosts. Now do you believe in ghosts?

Only *you* can answer that.

TRUE STORIES

More True Stories by Terry Deary ...

True Spy Stories
What's it like to be a spy? Glamorous and exciting? Just like James Bond? Find out in these true tales of international espionage.

True War Stories
What is war *really* like? Here are stories of sacrifices and massacres, of battles fought on horseback and in the trenches, at sea and on land.

True UFO Stories
Is there intelligent life on other planets? Have beings from outer space ever visited Earth? Whether or not you believe them, someone, somewhere at some time has sworn that each of these amazing stories is true.

TRUE STORIES

More True Stories by Terry Deary ...

True Detective Stories

Fascinating, frightening or just plain frustrating? These eight gripping stories show detective work as it really is. Sometimes truth can be stranger than fiction...

True Crime Stories

Read about highwaymen, pirates, murderers and kidnappers in these nine exciting real-life crime stories.

True Shark Stories

Terrifying, man-eating monsters? Or misunderstood creatures, persecuted by humans? Discover the truth about sharks, and make up your own mind, in these gripping tales of suspense, danger and courage.